THE DESTROYER™

CREATED BY WARREN MURPHY AND RICHARD SAPIR

Written by
Will Murray

Original Editor
Howard Mackie

Editor in Chief
Tom DeFalco

Reprint Editor
Glenn Herdling

Reprint Assistant
Pat Garrahy

Reprint Design
Larry Daley

Book Designer
Joe Kaufman

Cover art
Dorian Vallejo

Original Cover art
Joe Jusko
Dorian Vallejo
Earl Norem

HIS NAME IS REMO
pages 1-54

Art
Lee Weeks

Color
Greg Wright

Letters
Jack Morelli

GOLDEN RULE
page 56-93

Pencils
Mike Manley

Inks
Mike Manley
Al Williamson

Colors
Judy Johnson

Letters
Jack Morelli

HOW MANY NINJAS DOES IT TAKE TO SCREW UP A LIGHT BULB?
pages 95-134

Pencils
Lee Weeks

Inks
Chris Ivy
Win Mortimer
Mark Texeira
Lee Weeks

Colors
Christie Scheele

Letters
Jack Morelli

HOW THE THIEVING NINJA CAME TO BE
pages 135-140

Art
Steve Ditko

Color
Ed Lazellari

Letters
Jade Moede

THE DESTROYER ™   Originally published in magazine form as The Destroyer #1, #2, #3, & #4. Published by Marvel Comics, 387 Park Avenue South, New York, New York 10016. Copyright © 1990, 1991 Warren Murphy. All rights reserved. THE DESTROYER ™ and all prominent characters featured herein and the distinctive likenesses thereof are trademarks of Warren Murphy. All other material copyright © 1990, 1991 Marvel Entertainment Group, Inc. No part of this book may be printed or reproduced in any manner without the written permission of Warren Murphy and the publisher. Printed in The United States of America. First Printing October 1991.
ISBN #0-87135-844-1 GST #R127032852

10 9 8 7 6 5 4 3 2 1

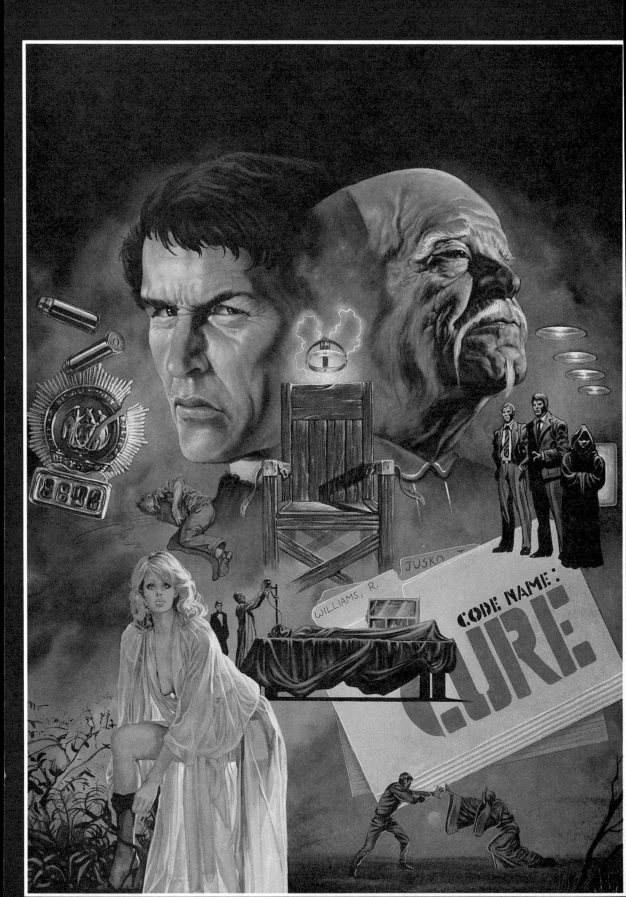

CODE NAME:

CURE

NORTH KOREA...

THE VILLAGE OF SINANJU ON THE WEST KOREA BAY...

A GUNMETAL CONNING TOWER BREAKS THE SLATE-GRAY WATERS...

AND ON THE BEACH, HAZEL EYES LIGHT WITH INTEREST. HIS WAIT IS OVER.

HIS NAME IS REMO

HIS FRAIL SHOULDERS RISE AND FALL WITH A SIGH OF DIS-APPOINTMENT. THE ROMANS WOULD HAVE SENT A DOZEN TRIREMES, HE THINKS. THE PHOENECIANS' PURPLE-SAILED GALLEYS WOULD HAVE ARRIVED WITH THE DAWN, NOT COME SKULKING IN DARKNESS.

BUT THAT WAS LONG AGO... BACK IN THE GLORY DAYS.

ER... PLEASE ACCEPT THIS TRIBUTE.

WHAT IS THIS?

A KRUGERRAND. YOU SPECIFICALLY REQUESTED THAT THE GOLD BE IN COIN FORM.

I PREFER GOLD TALENTS.

BUT I WILL ACCEPT THESE. NOW HAVE YOUR LACKEYS ATTEND TO MY LUGGAGE.

ALL RIGHT, LET'S GET THIS STUFF LOADED BEFORE THE NORTH KOREANS SPOT THE SUB!

DAMN! A COMMIE PATROL BOAT!

HOLD!

HEY! I NEED--

4

EMPEROR SMITH. IT IS A WORTHY NAME. PERHAPS HE WILL BE GOOD ENOUGH TO EXAMINE ME.

I HAVE BEEN LISTLESS OF LATE--

HE'S NOT *THAT* KIND OF DOCTOR.

HOW CURIOUS A LAND AMERICA MUST BE. YOU HAVE NO PROPER EMPEROR AND A PHYSICIAN RULES IN HIS STEAD. HIS SUBJECTS MUST BE EXCEEDINGLY HEALTHY.

THEY AREN'T. THAT'S WHY YOU'RE COMING TO THE USA. AMERICA IS SICK. AND YOU'RE GOING TO *CURE* IT.

YOU AND *REMO*.

AS THE USS DARTER SLIPS INTO THE WATERS OFF THE WEST KOREA BAY, ON THE OTHER SIDE OF THE WORLD...

8458

WILLIAMS, RE

... THE SUN RISES ON A SQUALID ALLEY IN NEWARK, NEW JERSEY.

RUN DMC

IT WARMS A FACE NOW COLD AND STIFF.

HIS NAME IS NOT IMPORTANT. HE SOLD HEROIN-- UNTIL SOMEONE CRUSHED HIS SKULL WITH A BASEBALL BAT.

AND SOMEONE WILL HAVE TO PAY FOR THAT CRIME. AND HE *DOES* HAVE A NAME.

IN THE MATTER OF THE PEOPLE VERSUS REMO WILLIAMS, WE THE JURY FIND THE DEFENDANT GUILTY OF MURDER IN THE FIRST DEGREE--

DUE TO THE EXTREME ATROCITY WITH WHICH THIS CRIME WAS COMMITTED, THE COURT FEELS IT HAS NO CHOICE BUT TO SENTENCE YOU TO DEATH BY ELECTROCUTION.

AND MAY GOD HAVE MERCY ON YOUR SOUL.

I DIDN'T DO IT! I WAS FRAMED! WHY WON'T ANYONE BELIEVE ME??

HEAR THAT?

THE JUDGE GAVE HIM THE CHAIR!

UNBELIEVABLE! HE WAS A COP!

TEN MINUTES, PADRE.

DON'T I EVEN GET A PRIEST?

KISS MY CRUCIFIX, WILLIAMS.

GO AHEAD, THERE'S A PILL AT THE BOTTOM. BITE IT OFF, BUT DON'T SWALLOW.

WHEN THEY PULL THE SWITCH, BITE DOWN HARD.

BITE DOWN HARD. THAT'S IT? NO LAST RIGHTS?

NOT MY DEPARTMENT. AND I'M ON A TIGHT SCHEDULE.

HAVE A GOOD DEATH.

6

LET'S SEE. BRING OUT CHEEKBONES. RAISE HAIRLINE. TIGHTEN EYES.

LOOKING INTO THE MIRROR IS ABOUT TO GAIN A NEW DIMENSION FOR YOU-- WHOEVER YOU ARE.

MASTER OF SINANJU, THIS IS DR. HAROLD W. SMITH. HE IS *CURE'S* DIRECTOR.

GREETINGS FROM THE HOUSE OF SINANJU, PEARL OF THE ORIENT, CENTER OF THE UNIVERSE, EMPEROR SMITH.

DR. SMITH WILL DO.

SINCE BEFORE WESTERNERS RECORDED HISTORY, MY ANCESTORS SERVED PHARAOHS AND KINGS. EGYPT KNEW US. ROME WAS SECURE BECAUSE SINANJU STOOD AT HER SIDE. PERSIA IS BLESSED TODAY BECAUSE SINANJU SOWED THE SEEDS OF HER GREATNESS.

IT'S CALLED IRAN NOW, AND IT'S A MESS.

TRADITION REQUIRES THAT I ADRESS CLIENTS AS EMPEROR.

ER, WHAT-EVER.

WHEN WILL I SEE THIS REMO?

HE'S SLEEPING RIGHT NOW.

GOOD. HE WILL NEED HIS STRENGTH.

HAS HE BEEN WEANED?

WEANED?

YES, YOUR MAN MacCLEARY HAS TOLD ME VERY LITTLE OF REMO, OTHER THAN THAT HE IS AN ORPHAN.

ER, I SEE. WHY DON'T WE JUST SHOW HIM TO YOU?

I SEE A POOR ACCIDENT VICTIM. WHERE IS THE FOUNDLING I AM TO TRAIN IN THE ART OF SINANJU??

THAT'S HIM. REMO.

AN *ADULT*?! WORSE, A LOWLY WHITE! I CANNOT TRAIN A WHITE! IT WOULD BE SACRILEGE!!

BUT HE'S BEEN SPECIALLY CHOSEN. NO FAMILY. FEW FRIENDS. WHEN THE BANDAGES COME OFF, NO ONE WILL RECOGNIZE HIM!

IT'S TOO LATE! AFTER THE AGE OF TWO, THEY ARE ALREADY BREATHING WRONG!

DO YOU KNOW WHAT YOU ASK OF ME? TO TEACH A WHITE THE SECRETS OF THE SUN SOURCE! NO ONE OUTSIDE MY VILLAGE HAS EVER BEEN SO PRIVILEGED.

LOOK, HE'S PERFECT! AN EX-MARINE, A FORMER COP, HE KNOWS HOW TO KILL.

SINANJU IS NOT THE ART OF KILLING. IT IS THE PERFECTION OF MIND AND BODY.

WHEN I AM DONE, MY STUDENT WILL BE THE PROUDEST OF PROFESSIONALS --A SINANJU ASSASSIN.

PLEASE, MASTER CHIUN. TRY.

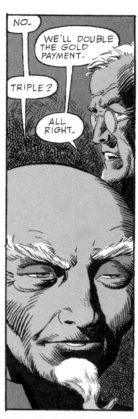

NO.

WE'LL DOUBLE THE GOLD PAYMENT.

TRIPLE?

ALL RIGHT.

SUMMON ME WHEN HE IS AWAKE.

WHITES. THEY ARE ALL ALIKE. BARBARIANS. I WILL TEACH THIS ONE A FEW TRICKS AND RETURN HOME.

IF ONLY MY WIFE HAD LIVED TO BEAR A PROPER SON, I WOULD NOW BE TRAINING A GRACEFUL KOREAN, NOT A BIG-NOSED CLOD.

LET ME GUESS. HEAVEN IS ALL BOOKED UP, SO THEY SENT ME TO TREASURE ISLAND, INSTEAD!

YOU'RE PRETTY FUNNY FOR A DEAD MAN.

MAYBE THIS WILL SOBER YOU UP.

LISTEN UP WHILE I TELL YOU A STORY. YEARS AGO, A YOUNG PRESIDENT SAW THAT THE U.S. WAS LURCHING TOWARD CHAOS. THE COURTS WERE CORRUPT. THE POLICE WERE OUTNUMBERED. IN SHORT, THE BAD GUYS WERE WINNING.

Constitution of the United States of America

HE FACED A CHOICE. SUSPEND THE CONSTITUTION LONG ENOUGH TO CLEAN IT UP, OR WATCH 200 YEARS OF DEMOCRACY VANISH TO THE SOUND OF A FLUSHING TOILET.

HE CREATED *CURE* INSTEAD.

TELL ME SOMETHING I DON'T KNOW BY HEART. I WALKED A NEWARK BEAT.

THAT'S YOU?

"IT'S ME. AND ONE OTHER PERSON. OFFICIALLY, WE DON'T EXIST. BECAUSE TO ADMIT WE EXIST IS TO ADMIT AMERICA SIMPLY DOESN'T WORK."

"AT FIRST, WE WORKED AS INFORMATION GATHERERS. BETWEEN OUR COMPUTERS AND OUR INFORMANTS, WE HELD BACK THE TIDE. FOR A WHILE I THOUGHT WE WERE WINNING. BUT THEN THE DRUG PROBLEM EXPLODED. CRIME AND CORRUPTION GOT WORSE. THEN THE PRESIDENT-- THE ONE WHO JUST LEFT OFFICE-- DECIDED THAT WE WOULD NEED AN ENFORCEMENT ARM."

"ONE MAN."   "*YOU*, REMO."

YOU'RE CRAZY!

CRAZY ENOUGH TO STEAL YOUR BADGE, PLANT IT NEXT TO A DEAD DRUG-PUSHER, BUY OFF THE JUDGE AND RIG THE ELECTRIC CHAIR SO THAT YOU DIDN'T REALLY DIE.

SO YOU WERE THE GUY WHO FRAMED ME!

AND YOU'LL BE THE MAN WHO DOESN'T EXIST. YOU'LL GO AFTER THE SCUM WHO ARE ABOVE THE LAW AND... UM... DEPHYSICALIZE THEM—

DEPHYSICAL-IZE?

THINK OF IT AS A LISCENSE TO KILL.

LIKE JAMES BOND, HUH?

HE ALWAYS GOT THE GIRLS AND THE CARS.

YEAH, WILLIAMS, SURE. EXACTLY LIKE JAMES BOND. YOU'D LIKE THAT, WOULDN'T YOU?

OKAY, I'LL GIVE IT A SHOT. AFTER ALL, WHAT CHOICE DO I HAVE?

GOOD. I'D HATE TO HAVE TO BURY YOU AGAIN.

DO YOU HAVE A NAME, OR IS IT A STATE SECRET?

CONRAD MacCLEARY. FRIENDS CALL ME CONN.

FROM YOU, I'LL SETTLE FOR MacCLEARY—

HELL OF A NAME FOR A GUY WHO'D FRAME AN INNOCENT COP.

THAT'S THE BIZ, WILLIAMS.

13

15

NOW THAT YOU ARE PROPERLY DRESSED FOR THE TASKS OF AN ASSASSIN, WE WILL BEGIN WORKING ON YOUR BREATHING!

I ALREADY KNOW HOW TO BREATHE, CHANG!

LESSON TWO: BREATHING CORRECTLY LEADS TO SPEAKING CORRECTLY.

AND I AM CHIUN, NOT CHANG.

I'LL LEAVE YOU TWO TO GET BETTER ACQUAINTED!

INHALE. EXHALE. FROM THE STOMACH, NOT THE LUNGS.

GOOD.

I'LL :OOF: GET YOU :WHOOF: FOR THIS :OOLF: MACCLE-- :OOF:

"GOOD NEWS AND BAD NEWS, SMITTY."

CHIUN THINKS HE CAN WORK WITH REMO. BAD NEWS IS HE SAYS IT'LL TAKE 15 YEARS, MINIMUM, TO MAKE HIM AN EFFECTIVE FIGHTING MACHINE.

WE'LL NEED HIM BEFORE THEN.

NO KIDDING. LET'S HOPE WE WON'T NEED HIM FOR ANYTHING BIG.

SNIK

THAT REMINDS ME. TIME FOR THE MID-DAY SITUATION CHECK.

HHMMMMMM

17

HMM. JUST ROUTINE MATTERS.

POSSIBLE SECURITY PROBLEM DEXTER DEFENSE INDUSTRIES

I'LL HANDLE THEM THROUGH THE USUAL LEGAL CHANNELS.

McLEAN, VIRGINIA. HOME OF DEXTER DEFENSE INDUSTRIES. MOTTO: "IF YOU WANT TO KILL, YOU GOTTA PAY THE BILL."

GENTLE-MEN.

DEXTER DEFENSE INDUSTRIES IS PROUD TO ANNOUNCE ITS LATEST PROTOTYPE.

THE DEXTER DEFENSE NUKE 'EM SPECIAL!

THIS IS A SEALED, ONE SHOT PISTOL. IT'S LIGHTWEIGHT, ACCURATE AND FIRES A LOW YIELD NUCLEAR MINI-WARHEAD!

ALERT! THIS UNIT IS NOW ARMED! ALERT!

18

THE SPECIAL WARHEAD DETONATES WITH A BLAST RADIUS OF 1600 FEET. THERE'S A THREE-STEP SAFETY TO PREVENT ACCIDENTAL FIRING. AFTER USE, THE MARKSMAN SIMPLY THROWS IT AWAY!

A TALKING GUN?

MAYBE IT SHOULD BE GIVING THE SALES PITCH ITSELF!

IT'S DISPOSABLE?

BECAUSE IT'S CHEAP. WE CAN CRANK THESE BABIES OUT ON THE ASSEMBLY LINE USING SEMI-SKILLED LABOR. THEY'LL MAKE THE SHOULDER-FIRED ROCKET OBSOLETE!

WHAT'S THE COST?

WE EXPECT TO MAKE THEM AVAILABLE TO THE DEFENSE COMMUNITY FOR ABOUT SEVEN THOUSAND DOLLARS PER!

NOT MUCH OF A KICKBACK IN THAT! I'VE PROCURED HAMMERS THAT COST MORE!

RIGHT! WE GOTTA SHOOT THIS THING DOWN.

VERY INTERESTING, DR. DEXTER. WHAT'S ITS' EFFECTIVE RANGE?

RANGE? JUST A MINUTE. I'LL CONSULT MY TECHNICAL STAFF.

TELL THEM IT'S BETWEEN ELEVEN AND THIRTEEN HUNDRED YARDS. MAYBE FOURTEEN IF YOU DON'T SHOOT INTO THE WIND.

RIGHT.

Ahem! THE NUKE 'EM SPECIAL CAN PUT ONE INTO A MOVING TARGET AT AN IMPRESSIVE SIXTEEN THOUSAND FEET.

THAT'S LESS THAN A MILE!

19

"YES, GENERAL. I BELIEVE YOU HAVE IT EXACTLY!"

"AND YOU SAY THE BLAST RADIUS IS SIXTEEN THOUSAND FEET?"

"THAT'S THREE MILES, DEXTER. THE SHOOTER MIGHT AS WELL BE STANDING ON GROUND ZERO."

ER... I SEE YOUR POINT.

OF COURSE, AS WITH ANY PROTOTYPE, THERE ARE A FEW MINOR BUGS TO BE WORKED OUT.

WAIT! COME BACK!

MAYBE WE CAN KNOCK THE PRICE DOWN TO FIVE HUNDRED PER UNIT!

WE'RE SUNK, REID.

THREE MILLION DOLLARS IN DEVELOPMENT AND YOU FORGET TO FIGURE IN THE FIRING RANGE!

I'M SORRY, DR. DEXTER BUT I'M A NUCLEAR PHYSICIST. NOT A TARGET SHOOTER!

FIX IT, OR YOU'RE FIRED, UNDERSTAND?

I'LL TAKE IT HOME AND WORK ON IT OVER THE WEEKEND.

I'M SURE DR. DEXTER WON'T MIND.

I WONDER IF SWITCHING TO A SOLID PROPELLENT WOULD HELP......

HOW DO I REPORT A FEDERAL CRIME?

FEDERAL BUREAU of [INVES]TIGATION

SEE THE SPECIAL AGENT IN ROOM 334.

THANKS.

THIS IS EASIER THAN I THOUGHT!

I WANT TO REPORT A SERIOUS EXTRA-LEGAL OPERATION IN RYE, NEW YORK. IT OPERATES UNDER THE COVER OF A--

--SANITARIUM...? FOLCROFT, BY ANY CHANCE?

YOU?! YOU'RE WITH THE FBI??

THEY THINK SO. SO DOES THE CIA. I HAVE AN OFFICE IN THE DEFENSE INTELLIGENCE AGENCY, BUT I HAVEN'T BEEN IN THERE IN YEARS!

YOU WERE WATCHED, WILLIAMS. I EXPECTED YOU TO PULL SOMETHING DUMB LIKE THIS. WHAT DID YOU THINK YOU WOULD ACCOMPLISH?

YOU HAVE A NEW FACE, NO I.D. AND YOUR FINGER-PRINTS ARE NO LONGER ON RECORD. YOU'RE A DEAD MAN. ASK ANYONE.

I'LL FIND SOMEONE WHO'LL BELIEVE ME!

YOU'D BETTER HOPE NOT. IF THE STATE LEARNS REMO WILLIAMS IS STILL ALIVE, YOU'LL BE THE FIRST GUY TO SIT IN THE HOT SEAT TWICE!

MAYBE. BUT YOU'RE NOT DRAGGING ME BACK TO THAT CRAZY OLD COOT WITHOUT A MAJOR FIGHT-IN TECHNI-COLOR!

I WOULDN'T WASTE MY TIME. BUT WHEN YOU REALIZE YOU DON'T HAVE ANYPLACE TO GO, YOU'LL COME BACK ON YOUR OWN.

23

24

"I HAVE AGREED TO COMPLETE YOUR TRAINING."

"MY EXECUTION YOU MEAN."

"FROM THIS DAY FOWARD, YOU WILL EAT NO MEAT EXCEPT FISH AND DUCK. YOU WILL HAVE RICE FOR BREAKFAST, LUNCH, AND DINNER. YOU WILL NOT SMOKE TOBACCO. AND YOU WILL ABSTAIN FROM ALCOHOL."

"WHAT ABOUT SEX?"

"I WILL TEACH YOU ABOUT SEX-- IF YOU ARE OBEDIENT."

"AND DO YOU ENJOY IT?"

"THAT WASN'T WHAT I MEANT. I ALREADY KNOW ABOUT SEX."

YEAH. USUALLY.

THEN YOU ARE DOING IT ALL WRONG. I WILL TEACH YOU HOW TO BEND WOMEN TO YOUR WILL. AND TO BREAK MEN LIKE TOYS.

YOU DO NOT YET REALIZE IT, REMO WILLIAMS, BUT YOU ARE VERY FORTUNATE. IN ALL OF HISTORY, NO WHITE PERSON HAS EVER BEEN OFFERED WHAT I AM ABOUT TO BESTOW UPON YOU.

YEAH? WHAT'S THAT?

IT IS CALLED SINANJU, AFTER MY HUMBLE VILLAGE WHERE IT ALL BEGAN.

KUNG FU STUFF, HUH?

PAH! KUNG FU WAS STOLEN FROM US! AS WAS KARATE, JUDO, AND ALL THOSE OTHER SILLY GAMES. SINANJU WAS THE SOURCE OF ALL. THE SUN SOURCE. IN SINANJU, YOU WILL LEARN PERFECTION. THROUGH ME, YOU WILL ATTAIN THE HIGHEST PINNACLE OF HUMAN ACHIEVEMENT.

HOW HIGH IS THAT IN INCHES?

WE WILL START HERE. TO THE PROFESSIONAL ASSASSIN, NO CASTLE, NO WALL, MUST DETER YOU FROM REACHING YOUR OBJECTIVE!

AGE BEFORE BEAUTY. IT'S AN OLD AMERICAN CUSTOM.

LOOK AT HIM GO! HE'S LIKE A SPRY OLD SQUIRREL!

THIS IS A SIMPLE ASCENT, SEE? THERE ARE CRACKS BETWEEN THE STONES FOR YOU TO GRIP!

WHAT ARE YOU WAITING FOR?

AN ELEVATOR! NO WAY I'M GOING UP THAT WALL!

UH-OH! MAYBE I SHOULDN'T HAVE MOUTHED OFF! HE'S COMING BACK!

AND HE DOES NOT LOOK HAPPY!

HOW THE HELL DID I GET WAY UP HERE? I DON'T EVEN REMEMBER HIM GRABBING ME!

CEASE STRUGGLING! YOU COULD FALL, AND I AM NO LONGER YOUNG. I MAY NOT CATCH YOU IN TIME!

HERE, THIS IS AN EASY PLACE. THE BRICKS ARE LOOSE AND EASILY TAKEN IN HAND. YOU MAY LET GO!

YOU MAY CLIMB, OR YOU MAY FALL!

WAIT! COME BACK! I DON'T KNOW THE FIRST THING ABOUT SCALING WALLS! I WAS A FOOT PATROLMAN!

LET GO? ARE YOU CRAZY?! HOW WILL I GET DOWN?!

IF I TOUCH GROUND ALIVE, I'M OUTTA HERE. THIS TIME I MEAN IT!

TOO LATE. I'M DEAD.

I CAN'T LOOK. PLEASE GOD, DON'T LET ME SUFFER...

OOFF!

YOU! I DON'T BELIEVE IT! NOBODY MOVES THAT FAST! YOU GOTTA BE TWINS!

I WILL TAKE THAT AS YOUR CLUMSY WAY OF SAYING THANK YOU.

THOSE BRICKS WEREN'T LOOSE. THEY WERE CRUMBLING! YOU TRIED TO KILL ME!

DO NOT BE RIDICULOUS! YOU HAVE NO INNER BALANCE! WE MUST WORK ON THAT BEFORE YOU AGAIN ATTEMPT VERTICALS!

27

28

OWWW. I THOUGHT I DODGED THAT ONE!

YOU DID. BUT YOU DID NOT DODGE THE RICO-CHET.

THAT WAS DELIBERATE, YOU LITTLE...

A TRUE ENEMY WOULD HAVE AIMED HIS ROCK AT YOUR HEART NOT YOUR FUNNY BONE.

JUST A BRUISE... AND I THINK HE PLANNED IT THAT WAY, SOMEHOW.

"THAT IS ENOUGH BULLET-DODGING FOR TODAY... TOMORROW I WILL SHOOT AT AT YOU WITH A TIMMY GUN."

"TOMMY GUN. AND NO WAY, YOU CHINESE SADIST."

"I AM KOREAN."

"YOU HAVE MY SYMPATHY."

I WILL IGNORE YOUR LACK OF RESPECT ONLY BECAUSE I HAVE SOME-THING IMPORT-ANT TO SHOW YOU.

THIS IS SHIVA, THE DESTROYER- DOES HE LOOK FAMILIAR?

NOT UNLESS I MET HIM IN A NIGHTMARE ONCE. SHOULD HE?

PERHAPS NOT- PERHAPS IT IS ONLY A COINCIDENCE. THE NAME.

WHAT'S ONLY A COINCIDENCE?

NEVER MIND. I MUST GO. WE WILL TRAIN AGAIN TOMORROW.

HOW IS HE COMING?

I REGRET TO SAY THAT YOU HAVE CHOSEN YOUR DESTROYER BADLY. I DO NOT THINK HE WILL SURVIVE HIS TRAINING.

TOUGH BREAK. FOR REMO.

YES, MR. PRESIDENT?

WE HAVE A SITUATION, SMITH. IS YOUR MAN READY?

IF HE IS NEEDED, HE WILL GO.

A HIGHLY UNSTABLE NUCLEAR WEAPON HAS FALLEN INTO CRIMINAL HANDS. A NUCLEAR PISTOL. THE MAN IN POSSESSION MAY NOT KNOW WHAT IT CAN ACTUALLY DO. THAT'S THE DANGER.

NUCLEAR!

IT FIRES A NUCLEAR BULLET. THIS CRIMINAL IS A FUGITIVE IN THE WASHINGTON D.C. AREA. WE DARE NOT INFORM THE LOCAL AUTHORITIES. THERE WOULD BE PANIC. IT'S UP TO YOUR MAN TO LOCATE AND DISARM HIM BEFORE HE PULLS THE TRIGGER!

I WILL GET RIGHT ON IT, SIR.

ONE LAST ITEM, SMITH. THE MAN WHO PULLS THE TRIGGER IS STANDING ON GROUND ZERO.

THAT'S A QUESTION I DON'T WANT TO HAVE TO ANSWER IN A PRESS CONFERENCE.

WHY, WHO WOULD BUILD SUCH AN ABSURD DEVICE?

NOW, IF YOU'LL EXCUSE ME, WE'RE EVACUATING THE WHITE HOUSE UNTIL THE CRISIS IS RESOLVED!

MacCLEARY, ACTIVATE THE DESTROYER.

33

35

36

NEVER MIND THAT, WHAT DO WE DO NOW?

I WILL GO IN THROUGH THE ROOF, YOU WILL ELIMINATE THE FOOLS WITH THE BOOM STICKS.

THE COPS? THEY'RE ON OUR SIDE!

IF THEY SHOOT, THAT MAN WILL SHOOT BACK, THEN THEY WILL ALL BE DEAD AND US WITH THEM. MacCLEARY SAID THIS WEAPON WILL DESTROY ALL LIFE FOR THREE MILES. THEY ARE DEAD EITHER WAY, ELIMINATE THEM.

I WAS A COP ONCE.

VERY WELL, I WILL ELIMINATE THEM. YOU GO IN AND DISARM THE CRETIN WITH THE NUCLEAR WEAPON.

YOU WANT TO KILL COPS, YOU'LL HAVE TO KILL ME FIRST!

KRAK
KRAK
KRAK
KRAK

"I DO NOT HAVE TIME TO KILL YOU, FOR IF WE DO NOT ACT SOON, WE WILL BOTH DIE!"

HE'S AT THE WINDOW AGAIN! OPEN FIRE! BRING THE BASTARD DOWN!

THIS IS JUST NOT MY DAY! I GOTTA GET THIS PIECE OF JUNK WORKING!

WONDER WHAT THIS LEVER DOES?

KLIK

GREAT! NOW IT'S HUMMING!

HMMMM

DAMN! NO FLASH, NO RECOIL. NOTHING. I'M GONNA GET MY BUTT SHOT OFF FOR SURE.

WISH I HAD A BEER TO HELP ME THINK.

HUMMMMM

UGH!

THAT WIND... LOSING CONSCIOUSS-NESS...

Uhhhh...

I CAN'T BELIEVE I'M DOING THIS. THE PERPETRA-TOR'S GOT A NUCLEAR WEAPON AND I DON'T EVEN HAVE MY BACKUP .22!

SO FAR, SO GOOD. OUTSIDE OF INHALING A CUBIC FOOT OF SOOT THAT IS...

THAT HUMMING FROM ABOVE... HE'S UP-STAIRS. HERE'S WHERE THAT DIPPY HOSTAGE NEGO-TIATION SEMINAR I TOOK AT THE ACADEMY PAYS OFF.

HEY, BUDDY... BE CAREFUL WITH THAT THING.

BACK OFF, COP!

HUMM MM MM

38

39

SO BE MY TICKET OUT OF HERE AND I MAY NOT MELT YOUR FACE—

HUMMMM

HEY, THEY'RE ALL DEAD! MAYBE THIS THING IS FINALLY WORK- ING!

COME ON, CHIUN. MAKE YOUR MOVE, FOR CRYING OUT LOUD!

HUMMMM

HUSTLE IT! WHAT'S THE MATTER? NEVER SUCKED ON A NUKE BEFORE?

OKAY, GET BEHIND THE WHEEL. AND NO TRICKS. I KNOW YOU'RE A COP. YOU LOOK LIKE ONE AND YOU TALK LIKE ONE. BE SMART AND YOU WON'T BLEED LIKE ONE—

THAT LITTLE KOREAN FINK! HE TOOK OFF ON ME! IT'S UP TO ME NOW. HERE GOES...

DUMB MOVE, COP!

REAL DUMB!

UGH!

HUMM KRUNCH

LUCKED OUT AGAIN, BUT I CAN'T KEEP RUN- NING LIKE THIS. I NEED A PLANE. AND AS SURE AS GOD MADE BEER, THE AIRPORTS ARE CRAWLING WITH COPS!

I KNOW! HOSTAGES! I'LL BAG A MESS OF HOSTAGES! THEN THEY'LL HAVE TO GIVE ME A PLANE. AND I KNOW JUST WHERE TO GET SOME, TOO--

HIS THIRD EYE SHOULD BE... HERE. ALTHOUGH CONSIDERING HE'S WHITE, IT MAY BE ON HIS BIG TOE.

Ah, HE STIRS!

Uhhhh... HOW LONG HAVE I BEEN OUT?

SINCE BIRTH!

HOW COULD YOU DO THIS TO ME?

ALLOWING YOURSELF TO BE TAKEN HOSTAGE! YOUR RECKLESSNESS MIGHT HAVE GOTTEN ME KILLED!

YOU! WHAT ABOUT ME? I WAS THE GUY WITH THE WARHEAD JAMMED BETWEEN HIS TONSILS. I COULD HAVE DIED TOO, Y'KNOW!

THAT IS OF NO CONSEQUENCE. YOU WHITES DIE ALL THE TIME AND ARE SELDOM MISSED, EXCEPT BY YOUR MOTHERS. I AM THE LAST MASTER OF SINANJU. MY VILLAGE DEPENDS ON ME.

DO NOT CONCERN YOURSELF WITH THEM. THEY MERELY SLEEP. THEIR LIVES ARE MY GIFT TO YOU.

WE GOTTA STOP THIS NUT! HE DOESN'T KNOW WHAT THAT GUN CAN DO. AND I DON'T THINK HE'D CARE IF HE DID!

WHAT DO YOU THINK YOU ARE GOING TO DO WITH THAT UNCLEAN CONTRAPTION?

I'M GOING TO FORMALLY INTRO- DUCE OUR HAIRY FRIEND TO A CLOUD OF DOUBLE-O BUCKSHOT. IF YOU'RE COMING, GET IN. MAYBE I CAN DROP YOU OFF AT A NICE SAFE BOMB SHELTER.

UNIT 55-- REPORT TO YOUR COMMANDER!

I DO NOT FEAR FOR MY OWN LIFE.

SURE, SURE.

42

EVERYONE HOLD YOUR POSITIONS. REPEAT: HOLD YOUR POSITIONS.

THE BUILDING HAS BEEN EVACUATED EXCEPT FOR ONE CLASSROOM. THERE ARE NO MORE THAN 25 HOSTAGES AT THIS TIME.

THIS IS WEIRD. WE'RE RIGHT IN THE MIDDLE OF THEM, BUT THEY DON'T EVEN NOTICE US!

CAN YOU TEACH ME TO DO THAT?

I JUST DID!

AND THE NEXT TIME WE SCALE A WALL, DO NOT EXPECT ME TO CARRY YOU!

NEXT TIME I'M TAKING THE STAIRS. WHAT'S OUR NEXT MOVE?

AH, EXCELLENT! HE IS ONLY BULLYING THEM! WE HAVE TIME FOR MY STORY. *SIT.*

WHAT I AM ABOUT TO TELL YOU IS KNOWN TO VERY FEW OF YOUR... KIND.

I CAME FROM A POOR FISHING VILLAGE. *SINANJU.*

IT WAS SO POOR, IN TIMES OF FAMINE, PARENTS WERE FORCED TO DROWN THEIR CHILDREN TO KEEP THEM FROM STARVING TO DEATH.

"WE CALL IT 'SENDING THE BABIES HOME TO THE SEA'."

"ONE DAY A MAN CAME TO OUR VILLAGE. A NAMELESS EXILE. HE WAS BLIND AND HIS CRIME WAS UNKNOWN. HE TAUGHT THE YOUNG MEN OF SINANJU HOW TO KILL.

"AND SO TO FEED OUR CHILDREN, THEY HIRED THEMSELVES OUT AS ASSASSINS AND PROTECTORS TO PRINCES AND KINGS!"

"SOMETIMES AS EXECUTIONERS,

"THIS MAN WAS THE FIRST MASTER OF SINANJU. HIS ACOLYTES BECAME FEARED THROUGHOUT ASIA AS THE NIGHT TIGERS OF SINANJU.

"WITHIN A FEW SHORT CENTURIES, THE HOUSE OF SINANJU BECAME THE MOST FAMOUS ASSASSINS IN THE ANCIENT WORLD. WE SAFEGUARDED THRONES FROM THE PHARAOHS TO THE CZARS. WE WERE HONORED. IN OUR WAY, WE WERE *ROYALTY.*

"EACH GENERATION, A NEW MASTER WAS BORN. OVER THE YEARS, OUR SKILLS WERE PERFECTED. WE THREW AWAY OUR WEAPONS. WE LEARNED TO FIGHT WITH OUR MINDS AND OUR BARE HANDS.

"OTHERS SAW OUR WORK AND COPIED US. THIS WAS HOW KUNG-FU, KARATE AND AIKIDO WERE BORN. AND THE THIEVING NINJA, TOO. BUT WE WERE FIRST, AND WE REMAIN THE BEST.

"ONE DAY, THE BAD TIMES RETURNED. A MASTER DIED BEFORE HE COULD TRAIN HIS PUPIL. THE SKILLS OF SINANJU WERE LOST FOREVER.

"AND THIS PUPIL, WHO WAS CALLED WANG, WENT OUT INTO THE WILDERNESS TO FAST. HE WAS IN DESPAIR. FOR ALREADY THE BABIES WERE BEING SENT HOME TO THE SEA FOR THE FIRST TIME IN GENERATIONS."

"THEN OUT OF THE SKY CAME A RING OF FIRE!

"AND IT SPOKE TO WANG."

"THE RING OF FIRE TOLD WANG THAT MEN DID NOT USE THEIR BODIES AS THEY SHOULD. THEY WASTE THEIR SPIRIT AND STRENGTH. IT TOLD WANG HOW TO UNLOCK HIS FULL POTENTIAL THROUGH CORRECT BREATHING.

"AND THEN THE LIGHT BURST, AND IN THAT INSTANT, MASTER WANG BECAME WHOLE."

AND WHEN WANG RETURNED TO HIS VILLAGE, HE PROCLAIMED A NEW ERA-- THE ERA OF THE *SUN SOURCE*. HE SLEW THE NIGHT TIGERS, SAYING THAT FROM NOW ON THE VILLAGE WOULD DEPEND ON ONE MAN-- THE *MASTER*.

SOUNDS LIKE A FAIRY TALE TO ME!

SILENCE! SINCE THE DAYS OF WANG THE GREAT, THE ASSASSINS OF SINANJU HAVE BEEN SUPREME. FOR WHAT WANG LEARNED FROM THE RING OF FIRE WAS THE ART OF *SINANJU!*

THAT'S WHAT YOU WANT TO TEACH ME? TO BECOME AN *ASSASSIN?*

TRY TO CONTAIN YOUR GRATI-TUDE.

YOU DON'T UNDERSTAND... IN AMERICA, ASSASSIN IS A DIRTY WORD. YEARS AGO, AN ASSASSIN MURDERED A POPULAR PRESIDENT AND HIS BRO-THER. THEY STRUCK DOWN AN IMPORTANT CIVIL RIGHTS LEADER. IT THREW MY COUNTRY INTO DE-SPAIR. I WANT NO PART OF THIS. I'D RATHER BE *DEAD.*

I THOUGHT THOSE SAME THOUGHTS WHEN I WAS YOUNG. FOR I DO NOT LIKE KILLING. BUT CHILDREN DEPEND UPON ME. HAD I A SON TO TRAIN, WE WOULD NOT BE HERE NOW. BUT DESTINY HAS CALLED ME TO AMERICA. AND CALLED YOU, TOO, REMO WILLIAMS.

FOR THE WORLD HAS FORGOTTEN THE HOUSE OF SINANJU. AND SOON, THE BABIES WILL BE SENT HOME TO THE SEA ONCE MORE.

NOW YOU SEE WHY I CANNOT RISK MY LIFE. IF I DIE, MY VILLAGE DIES. AND WITH IT, A FIVE THOUSAND YEAR TRADITION.

WELL, HAVE YOU NOTHING TO SAY?

I HAVE CHILDREN, TOO.

SOME OF THEM ARE COWERING UNDER OUR FEET. AND OUT THERE, THEY'RE DYING IN ALLEYS WITH NEEDLES IN THEIR ARMS. OR BEING USED BY CRIMINALS WHO THINK MONEY IS MORE IMPORTANT THAN THE FUTURE OF THIS COUNTRY. THE CHILDREN HARMED BY THESE CRIMES ARE *MY* CHILDREN.

WHEN I BECAME A COP, I TOOK A VOW TO PROTECT THEM.

I UNDERSTAND THIS. FOR I ALSO MADE A VOW TO PROTECT THE CHILDREN OF SINANJU.

I WILL MAKE A PACT WITH YOU, REMO WILLIAMS. I WILL SAVE YOUR CHILDREN IF YOU WILL DEAL WITH THIS MAN. THIS WAY, NO MORE CHILDREN-- YOURS OR MINE -- WILL HAVE TO *DIE.*

DEAL.

FOLLOW ME.

YOU WILL DISTRACT THIS MAN AND I WILL SEE TO IT THAT THE CHILDREN LIVE. THE REST IS UP TO YOU.

I'LL DISTRACT HIM ALL RIGHT. I HAVE JUST THE THING TO DO IT WITH, TOO.

MASTERS OF SINANJU IN TRAINING DO NOT SOIL THEIR HANDS WITH WEAPONS.

YOU JUST DO YOUR THING. I'LL HANDLE MY END *MY* WAY!

AN ACCIDENTAL DISCHARGE COULD JEOPARDIZE US ALL.

HURRY IT UP, WILL YOU??

LET ME SEE IT, FIRST. THESE DEVICES ARE NOTORIOUSLY UNRELIABLE.

HERE. AND BE CAREFUL. THIS IS THE WRONG WEAPON TO USE AROUND INNOCENTS.

BEFORE YOU GO, A FINAL MATTER.

DON'T SWEAT IT. ONE CLEAN SHOT IS ALL I'LL NEED.

THAT HAD BETTER BE A KOREAN GOOD LUCK SIGN.

IT WILL GIVE THAT LUNATIC SOMETHING TO AIM AT BESIDES CHILDREN.

WHAT HAPPENS IF I GET KILLED?

DO NOT WORRY. MacCLEARY PAID FOR YOUR TRAINING IN ADVANCE.

VERY FUNNY. NOW LET'S DO IT.

THE SEMINAR DIDN'T EXACTLY COVER THIS, SO I GUESS I'LL HAVE TO WING IT...

PIZZA DELIVERY!

NOK NOK

49

TODAY MUST BE HOOKY DAY. IT'S JUST YOU AND ME NOW.

YOU TRICKED ME!

WHAT THE HELL! I WAS SICK OF THOSE RUGRATS BAWLING ANYWAY- GUESS WHAT? I FINALLY GOT THIS THING WORKING!

WAY TO GO, CHIUN!

ONCE THE KIDS ARE OUT OF RANGE, I CAN MAKE MY MOVE!

NOW ALL I NEED IS A MOVE THAT WON'T GET ME KILLED...

NO CHANCE, CORNSUCKERS! I STILL GOT ME A HOSTAGE. I'LL TRADE HIM IN FOR A HELICOPTER AND TWO MILLION BUCKS!

IT'S ALL OVER, DEETZ! THROW THE WEAPON OUT THE WINDOW!

DO IT NOW, OR WE ALL GO NUCLEAR!

THEY MUST BE OUT OF RANGE BY NOW!

IT'S TIME!

STAY WHERE YOU ARE! ARE YOU NUTS?

YOU KNOW, I'M GETTING REAL TIRED OF YOUR CRAP, DEETZ. I DON'T THINK YOU'VE GOT THE STONES TO PULL THAT TRIGGER!

WHY DON'T WE JUST FIND OUT ONCE AND FOR ALL??

51

GURGLE...

Uhhh... WHAT HAPPENED? WHERE AM I?

HOLY HELL! HE'S DEAD. AND WHAT HIT HIM--A *FREIGHT TRAIN*?

WHAT THE HECK, IT'S NOT MY PROBLEM. I'M *OUTTA HERE*!

DON'T NEED THIS. BETTER LEAVE IT FOR THE CORONER. IT'LL MAKE LIFE EASIER.

THAT SINANJU BULLDOOKY MUST BE CONTAGIOUS. I WENT THROUGH THE POLICE BARRICADE SLICKER THAN LAMONT CRANSTON THROUGH A DARK ALLEY. BET EVEN CHIUN WOULD BE IMPRESSED!

Uh-OH! SPEAK OF THE DEVIL...

WERE YOU SUCCESS-FUL?

CHECK IT OUT.

THIS EVIL DEVICE MUST NEVER THREATEN ANOTHER CHILD.

HEY! MacCLEARY WANTED THAT BACK!

WHAT WHITES WANT AND WHAT THEY GET ARE TWO DIFFERENT THINGS.

BUT YOU MAY PRESENT HIM WITH THESE HARMLESS PIECES IF YOU WISH.

OR YOU MAY KEEP THEM AS A SOUVENIER TO REMIND YOU THAT TRULY INVINCIBLE WEAPONS ARE CARRIED ON THE ENDS OF WRISTS... NOT IN HANDS.

THAT REMINDS ME, I THOUGHT YOU CHECKED MY SHOTGUN? IT MISFIRED-- BOTH BARRELS!

AS YOU AMERICANS SAY-- I REST MY CASE!

YOU KNOW, CHIUN, SOMETHING WEIRD HAPPENED BACK THERE. I BLANKED OUT OR SOMETHING AND WHEN I CAME TO, THE GUY WAS DEAD. BUT I DON'T REMEMBER DOING IT!

IF YOU DID NOT, THEN WHO?

THAT'S EXACTLY WHAT I'M WONDERING...

END

54

GOLDEN RULE

BETWEEN PUERTO RICO AND THE DOMINICAN REPUBLIC LIES THE MONA PASSAGE, A TRANQUIL STRETCH OF TURQUOISE WATER THAT FOR NEARLY 500 YEARS HAS HELD A FABULOUS SECRET...

TWO SCUBA DIVERS DESCEND INTO IT'S IMMACULATE BEAUTY, THRESHING FLIPPERS SENDING THE NEON FISH SCURRYING. THEIR LIGHTS GO ON, FOR THEY SEEK SOMETHING VERY SPECIAL UNDER THE SHADOW OF A FANTASTIC CORAL ARCH.

IT'S ONLY THE FIRST DAY OF THEIR SEARCH. WITH 26 SUNKEN WRECKS TO PLUMB, NO ONE EXPECTS IT TO BE EASY. BUT TODAY, LADY LUCK WILL SMILE OVER THE MONA PASSAGE.

THE TWO SALVORS ARE GOING TO FIND THEIR PRIZE. AND THEY'RE GOING TO WISH THEY HADN'T.

I DID PROMISE THAT, YES, BUT THERE'S BEEN A *CHANGE.* THERE WILL BE *NO SPLIT.* BECAUSE THERE WILL BE NO TABLE TO DIVIDE.

HUH?

GET THE STONE, CONSUELO. AND BE GOOD ENOUGH TO COMMIT THOSE SYMBOLS TO YOUR INFALLIBLE MEMORY.

OKAY, MEL, I GOT IT!

YOU-- PUT IT OVER THE SIDE.

BUT-- BUT--

LOOKS *CHEAP.*

VERY WELL. SINCE YOU APPEAR TO BE PARALYZED WITH FEAR...

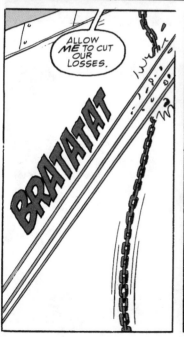

ALLOW *ME* TO CUT OUR LOSSES.

BRATATAT

I AM TRULY SORRY THAT THIS LITTLE ADVENTURE HAS TURNED OUT SO BADLY FOR YOU MEN.

SPLASH

HE'S GONNA *KILL* US! I CAN SEE IT IN HIS EYES!

SWIM FOR IT!

NO! NO!

I DON'T BLAME YOU MEN, REALLY. SOMETIMES THE INVESTMENTS OF GOLDEN RULE, LIMITED GO AWRY, MAKING IT NECESSARY TO *LIQUIDATE* OUR POSITIONS.

IT'S AT TIMES LIKE THIS THAT I LIKE TO INVOKE OUR COMPANY SLOGAN--

AAHHH!

"DO UNTO OTHERS---"

TONIGHT, THE WATERS OF THE MONA PASSAGE ARE NO LONGER TURQUOISE, BUT VERY NEARLY SCARLET-

FOLCROFT SANITARIUM, COVER FOR AMERICA'S SUPERSECRET SECURITY AGENCY, *CURE.*

YOU ASKED FOR ME, SMITTY?

YES, MacCLEARY. HOW IS REMO'S TRAINING PROGRESSING?

BETTER THAN LAST WEEK. HE'S ONLY TRIED TO ESCAPE *THREE* TIMES. A NEW LOW-- UNLESS YOU COUNT THE WEEK HE WAS LAID UP WITH A *SPRAINED NECK.*

SOMETIMES I THINK THAT THE MASTER OF SINANJU IS TRYING TO *KILL* HIM.

IF HE CAN'T SURVIVE THE *TRAINING,* HE'S NO GOOD TO *CURE.*

THERE'S BEEN *ANOTHER* URANIUM SHIPMENT THEFT. THIS TIME FROM A PROCESSING PLANT IN FERNALD, OHIO-

CONFIDENTIAL

THAT'S THE THIRD ONE THIS MONTH! TERRORISTS?

IT'S NOT WEAPONS GRADE MATERIAL. YET I'VE BEEN MONITORING A PATTERNLESS OUTBREAK OF RADIATION POISONINGS NATIONWIDE!

LOOK INTO IT, MacCLEARY.

ME? I WAS PLANNING TO GET SOUSED THIS WEEKEND! BESIDES, I HAVE A DENTIST'S APPOINTMENT THIS AFTERNOON. I'M GETTING A CAVITY FILLED!

KEEP IT. MY COMPUTER HAS TRACED A PARTIAL LICENSE PLATE TO A NEW YORK CITY TRUCKING FIRM. THAT'S THE ADDRESS. THE MAN'S NAME IS GROGAN.

HIS NAME IS REMO AND HE'S LEARNING TO HARMONIZE WITH THE UNIVERSE...

BUT FIRST HE HAS TO TAKE BABY STEPS.

SINCE YOU CONTINUE TO STUBBORNLY CLING TO YOUR FEAR OF HEIGHTS--

CUTTING THE HIGH WIRE BEFORE I WAS ACROSS DIDN'T HELP, CHIUN. I NEARLY BROKE MY NECK!

HAD YOU LANDED CORRECTLY, YOU WOULD NOT HAVE BEEN INJURED. AND YOU WOULD HAVE LEARNED THAT YOUR FEAR WAS WORSE THAN THE FALL. AS I WAS SAYING, WE WILL ATTEMPT A NEW APPROACH.

61

PRETEND WITH ME, REMO, THAT THESE LOGS ARE BALANCED OVER A GREAT RAVINE.

WHY? AND WHY THE BLINDFOLD?

FIRST, TO TEACH YOU THAT BALANCE HAS NOTHING TO DO WITH HEIGHT, BUT WITH THE BODY'S INNER HARMONY,

THE BLINDFOLD IS SO THAT YOUR WEAK WHITE MIND WILL NOT BE *DISTRACTED* BY YOUR SURROUNDINGS.

WHAT IS IT YOU HAVE AGAINST WHITE PEOPLE?

ONLY THAT THEY ARE NOT KOREAN.

THIS IS *STUPID.* I'M NOT CUT OUT FOR THIS. I'M A *COP.* OR I WAS UNTIL DR. SMITH AND CONN MacCLEARY FRAMED ME FOR THAT PUSHER'S MURDER.

YOUR MIND IS WANDERING. I CAN SENSE IT.

I'M OVER A GREAT RAVINE, OKAY?

DO YOU SEE THE GREAT RUSHING RIVER BELOW? IT IS VERY FAR BELOW, BUT YOU ARE NOT AFRAID BECAUSE I HAVE TAUGHT YOU TO BREATHE. AND HE WHO BREATHES PROPERLY CAN LEARN TO BANISH ALL FEAR.

GOOD. CONTINUE ALONG. YOU NO LONGER NEED MY GUIDANCE.

IF I CAN JUST DITCH THIS OLD COOT... I'LL GO TO MEXICO. THEY'LL NEVER FIND ME THERE. ESPECIALLY IF I GET ANOTHER FACE LIFT. SINCE THEY FAKED MY ELECTROCUTION, I DON'T EXIST. SHOULD BE EASY TO DISAPPEAR, IT'S A BIG WORLD.

64

NEW YORK CITY. FOR JACK GROGAN, IT'S THE END OF ANOTHER WORKING DAY...

AND INCIDENTALLY, THE LAST FIVE MINUTES OF HIS LIFE...

ABOUT DAMN TIME. I'VE BEEN HERE FOR HOURS. AND THIS NEW FILLING IS *KILLING* ME.

WHAT'S THE BEEF?

F.B.I. GROGAN, YOU'RE WANTED FOR QUESTION- ING...

SOMETHING ABOUT URANIUM.

KEEP YOUR HANDS WHERE I CAN--

UHHH!

BLAM
BLAM

DAMN, MUST BE GETTING *OLD*. SHOT HIM TWICE AND HE'S STILL BREATHING!

LISTEN, FRIEND, I NEED SOME ANSWERS AND YOU NEED AN AMBULANCE. LET'S *SWAP*.

GOLDEN... RULE... THAT'S ALL I... I... KNOW...

DEAD.

SORRY, PAL. YOU DIDN'T HOLD UP YOUR END. PARAMEDICS DON'T COME FOR CORPSES.

I BOTCHED THIS ONE *GOOD*. SMITH'LL HAVE MY BUTT. UNLESS HE CAN MAKE SOME- THING OUT OF *GOLDEN RULE*.

HOW DOES IT GO? "DO UNTO OTHERS AS YOU WOULD HAVE THEM DO UNTO YOU."

WILL HE LIVE, CHIUN?

OF COURSE. BUT FOR HOW LONG, NO ONE CAN SAY. HIS TRAINING FOR TODAY WAS EASY AS -- WHAT IS IT THAT YOU AMERICANS SAY -- FALLING OFF A LOG.

I THINK HE HAS A BAD HEART.

KEEP AT IT. SMITH MAY HAVE A BIG ASSIGNMENT FOR HIM SOON.

GOOD. PERHAPS THEN I WILL BE RID OF THESE FOOLISH WHITES.

I MISS MY VILLAGE OF SINANJU.

NOK NOK

SMITTY -- I DON'T KNOW HOW TO TELL YOU THIS, BUT--

STILL AT IT, HUH? SOMETHING WRONG WITH THE SYSTEM?

IT'S VERY STRANGE. I'VE REPLACED THE MICROCHIPS TWICE, BUT THE SYSTEM CONTINUES TO ACT UP. THE NEW CHIPS MUST BE DEFECTIVE!

WE ALL HAVE OUR BURDENS. MY ASSIGNMENT DIDN'T GO WELL. I HAD TO SHOOT OUR ONLY LEAD. DO THE WORDS GOLDEN RULE MEAN ANYTHING TO YOU?

THEY DO. FOR THE LAST THREE MONTHS, I'VE BEEN TRACKING CURIOUS TRANSACTIONS BY A PRECIOUS METALS BROKERAGE KNOWN AS GOLDEN RULE, LIMITED.

THEY ARE BUYING AND SELLING GOLD AT A FRANTIC PACE.

KEEP TALKING. I'M LISTENING. I JUST NEED AN ASPIRIN. I'VE HAD THIS WHOPPER OF A HEADACHE SINCE I LEFT THE DENTIST.

IT'S LIKE BUSINESS SUICIDE. THEY'RE SELLING OFF GOLD AT 20% BELOW ITS MARKET VALUE... WHILE SIMULTANEOUSLY BUYING MORE GOLD AT FULL PRICE THROUGH A SHELL CORPORATION.

SOUNDS LIKE A SENSIBLE BUSINESS STRATEGY TO ME. PROBABLY A SPIFFY TAX BREAK IN IT FOR THEM, TOO!

I THOUGHT YOU HAD YOUR... ER... *PROBLEM* UNDER CONTROL.

I DO. I ONLY DRINK TO WASH DOWN LIFE'S LITTLE UNPLEASANT-RIES. ASPIRIN. FOOD. OXYGEN. WANT ME TO LOOK INTO GOLDEN RULE?

NO. I BELIEVE THIS WOULD BE AN EXCELLENT OPPORTUNITY TO TEST REMO'S INVESTIGATIVE SKILLS.

WASTE OF TIME. HE HAS NONE. BESIDES, HE'S SEDATED. CHIUN PUT HIM THROUGH THE *WRINGER* TODAY.

TOMORROW, THEN. UNTIL I FIX THIS TERMINAL, WE HAVE NO INVESTIGATIVE OUTREACH. *CURE* IS PARALYZED.

WALL STREET...

REMEMBER, REMO. MacCLEARY WISHES US TO SIMPLY INVESTI-GATE THIS PLACE. THERE WILL BE NO *KILLING* WITHOUT FURTHER INSTRUCTION.

I WAS A *BEAT COP!* WHAT DO I KNOW ABOUT DETECTIVE WORK?

WE'RE HERE TO SEE MELDRUM RUST. *TROT* HIM OUT.

WHAT IS THE NATURE OF YOUR BUSINESS?

WE UNDER-STAND THAT HE'S BEEN BUYING LONG AND SELL-ING SHORT, CONTRARY TO EVERY RATIONAL PRINCIPLE OF THE FREE ENTERPRISE SYSTEM.

UH, HE'S OUT OF TOWN.

TELL HIM UNLESS HE WANTS HIS SCHEME TO BLOW UP IN HIS FACE, HE HAD BETTER CON-TACT US.

WE'LL BE AT THE WALDORF-ASTORIA. ROOM 334. GOT THAT?

I DO NOT UNDERSTAND. WE ACCOM-PLISHED *NOTHING.*

AND YOU VIOLATED EVERY RULE OF ESPION-AGE BY EXPOSING YOUR INTENTION.

HEY, I'M *NEW* AT THIS. I JUST FIGURE INSTEAD OF SCREWING AROUND CHASING THIS GUY, LET HIM COME TO *US.*

NOW, WHILE WE SLIP INTO OUR DESIGNER RADIATION SUITS, I WILL TREAT YOU, MY DEAR SECRETARY AND PARAMOUR, TO THE COMPLETE STORY OF THE *STONE*.

FOR CENTURIES, MEN HAVE SOUGHT THE FABLED PHILOSOPHER'S STONE-- WHICH COULD TURN BASE METALS INTO *PURE GOLD*.

SOME THOUGHT IT WAS A MYTH. IT WAS NOT. THE MOORISH KINGS OF SPAIN POSSESSED IT. BUT THEY LACKED THE *OTHER* INGREDIENT, WITHOUT WHICH THE STONE WAS A MERE BAUBLE.

"*I*N THE 16 TH CENTURY, THE STONE FELL INTO THE HANDS OF FRANCISCO DE BOBADILLA, AGENT FOR KING FERDINAND OF SPAIN.

"*A*FTER A SLAP-DASH INVESTIGATION, BOBADILLA SENT THE HAPLESS COLUMBUS BACK TO SPAIN IN *CHAINS*.

"FERDINAND SENT BOBADILLA TO HISPANIOLA, NOW CALLED THE DOMINICAN REPUBLIC, TO LOOK INTO CHARGES OF INCOMPETENCE LODGED AGAINST ITS GOVERNOR, CHRISTOPHER COLUMBUS!

"*YES... THAT* COLUMBUS.

"BUT COLUMBUS CONVINCED FERDINAND OF HIS INNOCENCE AND THE KING'S WRATH WAS DIRECTED AT BOBADILLA. HE SUMMONED THE UNFORTUNATE MAN HOME.

"*B*OBADILLA KNEW HIS ONLY CHANCE WAS TO APPEASE HIS LIEGE.

"*B*OBADILLA, USED IT TO TURN A LEAD TABLE INTO GOLD AND SENT IT TO FERDINAND IN HOPES OF SPARING HIS LIFE.

"*D*ESPERATE, HE FINALLY OBTAINED A TINY QUANTITY OF THE ELUSIVE SUBSTANCE THAT, WITH THE STONE, ALLOWED THE ANCIENT ALCHEMISTS TO MAKE THE TRANSMUTATION.

"*B*UT THE GALLEON CARRYING IT TO SPAIN WENT DOWN IN A HURRICANE -- ALONG WITH 25 OTHERS. THAT WAS IN *1502*.

BUT WHAT WILL WE DO WHEN THE STONE'S *USED UP?*

BY THAT TIME, MY DEAR, I WILL HAVE CORNERED THE WORLD'S *TRUE* GOLD. ONLY THEN I WILL REVEAL THE TRUTH. IN THE ENSUING CHAOS, I WILL CONTROL THE WORLD'S GOLD MARKET.

IT WILL BE THE BEGINNING OF THE *TRUE* GOLDEN RULE, AND I WILL BE THE GOLDEN *RULER!*

WHY NOT JUST KEEP *THIS* STUFF? IT'S CHEMICALLY IDENTICAL TO NATURAL GOLD, ISN'T IT?

TRUE, BUT *STONIUM*-- AS I CALL ALCHEMICAL GOLD-- HAS ONE UNFORTUNATE DRAWBACK. IT'S *RADIOACTIVE.*

NOW, YOU WANTED TO SEE ME ABOUT SOMETHING?

TWO STRANGE MEN CAME TO SEE YOU. THEY DEMANDED TO KNOW WHY YOU HAVE BEEN BROKERING GOLD AT SUCH LOW PRICES. I CAN'T IMAGINE THEY WERE GOVERNMENT AGENTS. THEY LEFT A HOTEL ROOM NUMBER WHERE THEY CAN BE REACHED.

BRUNO! MILES!

GO TO THE ADDRESS MISS CASTRO-BRUJA GIVES YOU. *KILL* ANYONE YOU FIND-- AFTER YOU EXTRACT THE REASON FOR THEIR INTEREST IN MY BUSINESS.

PARTY TIME, DUDES AND DUDETTES!!

BRAICH!

LET'S JUST GET THIS *OVER* WITH BRUNO! NO WATCHING THEM *BLEED TO DEATH* THIS TIME, O.K.?

I MUST BE OUT OF MY MIND TO COME BACK AFTER ALL I'VE BEEN PUT THRO--

OOFF!!

DON'T LOOK NOW, BUT I JUST TRIPPED OVER A STIFF.

HAVE A LITTLE PROBLEM HERE?

NO. TAKE OUT THE GARBAGE.

IT WILL BEGIN TO STINK SOON.

WHAT ABOUT THESE BODIES?

I WAS REFERRING TO THEM.

WOULDN'T IT BE EASIER FOR US TO SNEAK OUT OF THE HOTEL?

AFTER MY PROGRAM, PERHAPS...

I WOULDN'T WAIT THAT LONG. YOUR OTHER PLAYMATE'S DISCOLORING THE SIDEWALK -- AND DRAWING POLICE ATTENTION.

I WILL LEAVE THEM TO YOU, REMO. AS A FORMER MEMBER OF THEIR FRATERNITY, YOU NO DOUBT SPEAK THEIR LANGUAGE.

NOW WHAT?

RING RING

REMO? MACCLEARY HERE. ANY PROGRESS?

YES AND NO -- WE STIRRED THEM UP. THEY SENT OUT A BUNCH OF GOONS. TRIED TO KILL US, BUT CHIUN KILLED THEM FIRST. WE'RE HIP DEEP IN BODIES, AND I CAN'T PULL HIM AWAY FROM HIS FREAKING SOAP OPERA.

74

FOLCROFT SANITARIUM...

IS HE DRUNK, DOC?

I DON'T KNOW WHAT MacCLEARY'S PROBLEM IS. HE SHOWS SIGNS OF RADIATION POISONING.

BUT I CAN'T IMAGINE HOW THAT COULD BE.

THIS GEIGER COUNTER SHOULD PUT THAT THEORY TO REST.

GOOD LORD! I'M ACTUALLY GETTING A READING!

KLIK KLIK

THIS IS ASTONISHING! HIS TEETH SEEM TO BE RADIOACTIVE!

KLIK KLIK
KLIK
KLIK

GOLD TEETH?? WHAT A WASTE OF PRECIOUS METAL!

THIS FILLING COULD BE THE CAUSE.

PLEASE LEAVE US ALONE WHILE I RUN FURTHUR TESTS!

GO TO YOUR ROOM, REMO. I MUST SPEAK WITH MY EMPEROR.

WHEN AM I GOING TO MEET THIS EMPEROR OF YOURS?

IF YOU ARE LUCKY, NEVER. FOR TO BEHOLD HIS COUNTENANCE WOULD MEAN YOUR DEATH.

I'LL TRY TO KEEP THAT CHEERY THOUGHT IN MIND...

RADIOACTIVE? MacCLEARY??

THAT IS WHAT THE *PHYSICIAN* TOLD ME. I DO NOT UNDERSTAND IT EITHER.

MacCLEARY NEITHER SPOKE LIKE A RADIO, NOR WAS HE ACTIVE. IN TRUTH, HE WAS *SENSELESS!*

ER... I WILL EXPLAIN IT LATER, MASTER CHIUN... BUT I FAIL TO UNDERSTAND WHY YOU KILLED THE ATTACKERS.

THEY WERE *IMPOLITE,* THEY DISTURBED MY BEAUTIFUL DRAMAS.

UNNECESSARY BODIES RAISE QUESTIONS. AND ONE PRISONER COULD HAVE PROVIDED US WITH SOME *ANSWERS.*

WE HAVE ALL THE ANSWERS WE NEED, REMO AND I PRESENTED OURSELVES TO THEM, AND THEY SENT *BRUTES* TO KILL US...

I SUGGEST WE KILL THEM ALL. THEIR MISCHIEF WILL *DIE* WITH THEM.

NOT YET. WE MUST UNCOVER THE PURPOSE FOR THEIR PUZZLING GOLD TRANSACTIONS. IF ONLY MY COMPUTERS WERE WORKING...

TONIGHT, YOU AND REMO WILL BREAK INTO GOLDEN RULE. GO THROUGH THEIR RECORDS. DIG UP WHAT YOU CAN.

AND *THEN* MAY WE ELIMINATE THE EVIL ONES?

NO. BRING BACK ANY PROOF TO ME. I WILL DECIDE THEN.

NOT *AGAIN!* NO! YOU'RE NOT GETTING ME TO SCALE ANOTHER BUILD-ING!

IT WILL BE SIMPLE. FIRST YOU FIND THE BUILDING'S CENTER. THIS IS IMPORTANT. FOR YOU ARE *NOT* GOING TO CLIMB AGAINST GRAVITY... BUT USE THE BUILDING'S INNER FORCE TO LIFT YOU UP.

SOUNDS LIKE *ZEN CRAP* TO ME.

SINANJU IS NOT CRAP, UNGRATEFUL WHITE THING!!

IT IS THE *SUN SOURCE.* THE SEED FROM WHICH *ALL MARTIAL ARTS* FLOWERED IT--

Uh-Oh. TROUBLE. RENT-A-COP TROUBLE.

THEY'VE BOXED US IN TIGHT. NOW WHAT DO WE DO?

WE POSTPONE YOUR CLIMBING LESSON ONCE AGAIN.

SUITS ME.

WE FOUND THESE... *TWO* SKULKING OUTSIDE THE BUILDING, MR. RUST.

DO UNTO OTHERS

NICE MOTTO. TOO BAD YOU WENT FOR THE ECONOMY VERSION. KINDA DISTORTS THE *SPIRIT*.

I AM *MELDRUM RUST*, CEO OF GOLDEN RULE LIMITED.

AS YOU ARE DOUBTLESS *AWARE*.

PERHAPS YOU WILL BE GOOD ENOUGH TO EXPLAIN YOURSELVES WHILE I *MULL* TURNING YOU OVER TO THE AUTHORITIES.

I AM *CHIUN*, MASTER OF SINANJU.

JUST CALL ME *REMO*.

Ah, CONSUELO. I BELIEVE YOU TWO HAVE ALREADY *MET* MY DELIGHTFUL SECRETARY.

YES. THOSE ARE THE ONES.

THANK YOU, CONSUELO. NOW, GENTLEMEN, WOULD YOU CARE TO DIVULGE YOUR AFFILIATION? *S.E.C.*? *F.B.I.*? THE *I.R.S.* PERHAPS?

WHAT IS HE BABBLING ABOUT, REMO? I SPEAK ENGLISH, NOT AMERICAN...

LET ME HANDLE THIS...

CUT THE CRAP, RUST. WE *KNOW* ALL ABOUT YOUR SCHEME. SELLING GOLD CHEAP AND BUYING IT AT FULL MARKET PRICE.

OH, AND PRECISELY WHAT *AM* I UP TO?

YOUR TURN-- I GOT THE BALL ROLLING.

79

WHAT THE HELL KIND OF STUNT WAS *THAT?* YOU JUST ACCEPTED A *BRIBE!*

NO, I ASKED FOR THE GOLD TO BE SENT TO SMITH. IT IS SMITH'S GOLD. IF IT IS *TRUE* GOLD.

IT MAY BE *CURSED.* WORTHLESS.

WHAT MAKES YOU SAY THAT?

"ONCE THERE WAS A MASTER OF SINANJU NAMED *YI* WHO WAS IN THE SERVICE OF A MOORISH KING OF SPAIN.

"*THIS* MOORISH KING WAS BESET BY A PRETENDER. BUT HE KNEW NOT *WHICH* PRINCE COVETED HIS CROWN. HE OFFERED MASTER YI A SUM OF GOLD TO EXPOSE AND ELIMINATE THE CULPRIT.

"*YI* DID THIS AND TO HIS DELIGHT WAS PAID *TWICE* THE GOLD SUM PROMISED.

"*HE* RETURNED TO MY ANCESTRAL VILLAGE OF SINANJU AND PLACED THE KING'S GOLD WITH HIS OWN.

"WITHIN A MONTH, MASTER YI FELL *SICK.*

"*THAT* VERY YEAR, HE *DIED.*

"*BEFORE* HIS DEATH, YI PRONOUNCED THE GOLD CURSED AND ORDERED IT THROWN INTO THE SEA.

"AND HE SAID TO HIS PUPIL -- THE *NEXT* MASTER -- THAT FROM THAT DAY FOWARD NO MASTER WOULD ACCEPT PAYMENT *BEYOND* WHAT HAD BEEN AGREED UPON.

"SAID PAYMENT BEING CURSED BY THE GODS AND *TAINTED.*

81

NICE FAIRY TALE. WHAT DOES IT HAVE TO DO WITH US?

YOUR EMPEROR MAY KNOW.

ODD. RADIATION POISONING CASES ARE *SPREADING*. YET THEY SORT INTO NARROW VOCATIONAL CATEGORIES. JEWELERS. DENTISTS. COMPUTER TECHNICIANS.

THERE *MUST* BE A COMMON THREAD I'M OVERLOOKING...

GREETINGS, EMPEROR SMITH.

WHAT ON EARTH?

THE EVIL ONE'S GOLD HAS ARRIVED!

BWAAM

BEHOLD!

REEEE SNAP

MY *SCREEN!* IT'S ACTING UP AGAIN!

NO DOUBT, IT IS THE GOLD. THE FIEND, RUST, IS INFECTING THE WORLD WITH *POISON GOLD!*

HOW CAN GOLD BE *POISON*?

SORCERY. THAT MAN RUST IS A FOUL *WIZARD.*

THERE MUST BE A *RATIONAL* EXPLANATION. WHY WOULD GOLDEN RULE BE STEALING URANIUM AND SELLING GOLD AT MARKDOWN PRICES?

URANIUM AND *GOLD?* ONE MINUTE... MacCLEARY... HIS *FILLINGS* WERE GOLD.

DENTISTS. JEWELERS. COMPUTER TECHNICIANS. THEY *DO* HAVE SOMETHING IN COMMON— THEY WORK WITH *GOLD.*

OH GOD... MY *MICROCHIPS!*

KLIK
KLIK
KLIK

NO WONDER MY SYSTEM'S BEEN MISBEHAVING! MY MICROCHIPS ARE MADE FROM RADIOACTIVE GOLD!

THIS IS *SERIOUS.* COMPUTERS RUN OUR DEFENSE NETWORK!!

TIK
TIK
TIK
TIK

YOU SEE, EMPEROR? I KNEW THE GOLD WAS CURSED WHEN THE WICKED ONE OFFERED *TWICE* MY REQUEST!

HE GAVE YOU *DOUBLE* HOPING THE RADIATION WOULD KILL YOU!

I ADMIT TO FEELING A TRIFLE FAINT, BUT THE AIR IN THIS COUNTRY IS QUITE *ABOMINABLE.*

WITH NATIONAL SECURITY AT STAKE, I'M SANCTIONING YOU TO ELIMINATE RUST AND EVERYONE CONNECTED WITH GOLDEN RULE. THEIR MAD SCHEME MUST BE *STOPPED!*

THEIR *HEADS* WILL ADORN YOUR CASTLE FENCE BY SUNDOWN!

NO! I DON'T WANT THEIR *HEADS!* TAKE CARE OF THIS *QUIETLY!*

HOW FOOLISH. A FEW HEADS TODAY MEANS FEWER ENEMIES TOMORROW. BUT IT IS *SMITH'S* COUNTRY.

AS YOU WISH, EMPEROR.

DR. GREELEY, ABOUT MacCLEARY...

WARM UP THE SENORITAS. *MEXICO*, HERE I COME!

REMO! WHERE ARE YOU GOING?!

ME? I WAS JUST GOING FOR *A...A WALK.*

Uh... I THOUGHT I COULD USE SOME *NORMAL* EXERCISE FOR A CHANGE.

NEVER MIND. WE HAVE A NEW TASK. MY EMPEROR HAS FINALLY SEEN THE WISDOM IN ALLOWING US TO DISPOSE OF HIS ENEMIES.

DISPOSE?

I WILL EXPLAIN ON THE WAY. LEAVE YOUR BAG WHERE IT IS. YOU MAY ATTEMPT ANOTHER FOOLHARDY ESCAPE *TOMORROW.*

RIGHT. I'M GOING TO *DROP* EVERYTHING AND FOLLOW HIM TO HELL AND' GONE LIKE A FAITHFUL BOY SCOUT.

THEN AGAIN, THIS *IS* THE SAME GUY WHO SNUFFED TWO HOODS BECAUSE THEY INTERRUPTED HIS FAVORITE *SOAP.*

SAYING NO *COULD* GET ROUGH.

QUICKLY! THROUGH THE SECRET DOOR!

PREPARE TO *DIE*, ENEMIES OF AMERICA?

IT IS A SINANJU *TRADITION* TO STRIKE FEAR IN THE HEARTS OF ONE'S ENEMIES.

ALSO, IT IS GOOD ADVERTISING.

YEAH? AND IS IT TRADITIONAL TO BE *TRAPPED*? BECAUSE THERE GOES THE VAULT DOOR!

NEVER FEAR, REMO. THERE IS NOT A DUNGEON BUILT THAT CAN *HOLD* A MASTER OF SINANJU!

I DO NOT UNDERSTAND... IT RESISTED MY NAILS...

MAYBE THERE'S A *TELEPHONE* IN ONE OF THESE DRAWERS. WE CAN CALL FOR HELP.

NONSENSE. ONCE I FIND THE *WEAK SPOT*, THIS WALL WILL *SHATTER* AT THE MEREST-- HUHHHH...

HEY! WHAT'S *WRONG*?!

IT IS THE GOLD. IT IS ACCURSED.

WHAT?

IT IS TELEVISIONACTIVE. IT DISRUPTS THE PERFECT HARMONY OF MY MAGNIFICENT CONSTITUTION.

I DON'T FEEL ANYTHING.

YOUR HARMONIES ARE HARDLY PERFECT.

JUST HANG ON.

IF THIS STUFF IS SO DEADLY, HOW DO THEY KEEP IT FROM KILLING EVERYONE IN THE BUILDING?

SOFT. LIKE GOLD. OR LEAD. LEAD!

HANG ON, CHIUN. I'M GOING TO TRY SHUTTING EACH ONE OF THESE DRAWERS.

I AM DYING, AND YOU ARE SUDDENLY CONCERNED WITH NEATNESS!

ALL SET. TRY STANDING UP NOW.

I FEEL... STRONGER... MY VIGOR RETURNS! HOW?

THE VAULT IS LINED WITH LEAD TO SEAL OFF RADIATION. I JUST BLOCKED THE RADIA--

CEASE YOUR WITLESS PRATTLING! STAND ASIDE!

87

89

BOOM

AAAHHH!!

YOU :COUGH: DID THAT :COUGH: ON PURPOSE!

I HAD MY ORDERS.

DID YOU *HAVE* TO KILL THE *GIRL*, TOO?

ASSASSINS DO NOT PROVIDE EXEMPTIONS ON THE BASIS OF *GENDER*. YOU WILL LEARN THIS AS WE GO ALONG.

DO YOU SUPPOSE THEY TURNED TO GOLD, TOO?

NO. THE PHILOSOPHER'S STONE CAN ONLY TURN BASE *METAL* INTO GOLD. THOSE TWO WERE BASER THAN LEAD. THEY WERE *DUNG*.

LISTEN. I SAVED YOUR LIFE BACK THERE.

POSSIBLY.

DO ME A FAVOR? LOOK THE OTHER WAY WHILE I CUT OUT?

DONE.

THANKS! I WON'T *FORGET* THIS!

I AM *CERTAIN* YOU WILL NOT.

ATTENTION! FLIGHT 334 NOW BOARDING!

HOME FREE. NO MORE CHIUN, NO MORE FOLCROFT. I HOPE THEY HAVE PLASTIC SURGEONS IN ACAPULCO.

POIT

STAND BACK. I'M A DOCTOR. THIS MAN'S ILL! HELP ME GET HIM TO A COUCH.

MMMM. MUST'VE DOZED OFF. WONDER IF WE'VE LANDED YET...

YOU -- YOU TRICKED ME, YOU LITTLE --

YOU ASKED ME TO LOOK THE OTHER WAY, THIS I DID.

YOU DID NOT ASK ME TO AID AND ABET YOUR INGRATITUDE TO THOSE WHO PLACED YOU IN THE EXALTED STATE OF SINANJU DISCIPLE. MY ALLEGIANCE IS WITH MY EMPEROR.

YOU'LL BE INTERESTED TO KNOW THAT THE RADIOACTIVE GOLD HAS BEEN DESTROYED. RUST AND THE WOMAN WERE PRACTICALLY BOILED ALIVE.

NOT WHAT I'D CALL A HAPPY ENDING.

OH, I DON'T KNOW. RUST PLANNED TO FLOOD THE WORLD WITH RADIOACTIVE GOLD UNTIL GOLDEN RULE HAD CORNERED THE GOLD MARKET. MIGHT'VE WORKED, TOO.

HOW MANY NINJAS DOES IT TAKE TO SCREW UP A LIGHT-BULB?

THE PENTAGON.

BUILT ON A FORMER MUDFLAT CALLED "HELL'S BOTTOM", ON THE VIRGINIA SIDE OF THE POTOMAC, IT SERVES AS HEADQUARTERS TO THE DEPARTMENT OF DEFENSE, ARMY, NAVY, AND AIR FORCE. FEW REALIZE THAT DESPITE ITS FORTRESS-LIKE APPEARANCE, IT'S REALLY THE WORLD'S LARGEST OFFICE BUILDING. NEARLY 23,000 PEOPLE TOIL BEHIND ITS HELLENIC LIMESTONE FACADE. IT'S A VIRTUAL SELF-CONTAINED WORLD WITH ITS OWN POST OFFICE, POLICE AND FIRE DEPARTMENTS, TELEVISION STATION, INFIRMARY, SUBWAY STOP, HELIPORT, SHOPS, AND PHONE EXCHANGE.

THERE ARE PARKING SPACES FOR 10,000 VEHICLES, 100,000 MILES OF TELEPHONE CABLE AND 15 MILES OF MESSAGE-CARRYING PNEUMATIC TUBING. ITS RESTAURANTS SERVE OVER 15,000 MEALS A DAY.

THE PENTAGON IS EQUIPPED WITH EVERY CONVENIENCE OF A MODERN OFFICE BUILDING. EXCEPT ELEVATORS.

ITS INCONVENIENCES INCLUDE A LABYRINTHIAN CORRIDOR SYSTEM SO VAST THAT EVEN LONG-TIME EMPLOYEES CAN GET HOPELESSLY LOST.

AND THEN THERE ARE THE ROACHES.

ADMIRAL BLACK-BIRD'S CAR. I'M HERE TO PICK HIM UP.

GO RIGHT IN. I'LL INFORM HIS OFFICE YOU'RE HERE.

OFFICIALLY, THE PENTAGON HAS NO COCKROACH PROBLEM...

NOT EVEN HERE, IN THE UPPER BASEMENT, SET ASIDE FOR V.I.P. PARKING.

GUESS I HAVE TIME FOR A SMOKE...

RESERVED FOR ADMIRAL BLACKBIRD

ZiiiNG

PWANG

THE PROBLEM WITH COCKROACHES IS THAT THEY'RE CRAFTY CREATURES. THEY SCUTTLE OUT ONLY AFTER DARK. AND THEY RETREAT FROM LIGHT. YOU CAN BE INFESTED AND NEVER KNOW IT.

WHAT THE HECK WAS THAT? SOUNDS LIKE SOMEONE DROPPED A MIGHTY FAT COIN.

MUST BE THIS GLEAMING THING HERE. LOOKS BIG. MAYBE ONE OF THOSE OLD SUSAN B. ANTHONY DOLLARS.

THE WILEY COCKROACH DOES ALL HIS BUSINESS IN THE DARK. IF YOU'RE NOT CAREFUL, HE'LL EVEN GET INTO YOUR REFRIGERATOR...

TAKING WHATEVER PLEASES HIM...

AND LEAVING BEHIND UNWANTED PRESENTS.

WHAT THE *HECK*? THIS AIN'T MONEY.

AHHH!

PAT PAT PAT PAT

LOOK AT THIS. I'M BLEEDING LIKE A STUCK PIG. BETTER TIE IT OFF BEFORE I'M DRAINED WHITE!

AND HAVING SATIATED HIS NOCTURNAL HUNGER, SLIPS QUIETLY BACK INTO HIS LAIR. UNSEEN. UNSUSPECTED.

DAMN THING NEARLY TOOK MY FINGER OFF. SOME MILITARY JOKER MUST'VE DROPPED IT. IRRESPONSIBLE JERKS!

"RESERVED FOR ADMIRAL BLACKBIRD"

YEAH, THAT'S WHAT I'LL DO. SUE. I'M SICK OF PLAYING MY NUMBER FOR NICKEL RETURNS. LAWYERS GIVE BETTER ODDS ANYWAY.

BETTER DOWN A QUICK MARTINI BEFORE I SEE THE PRESIDENT.

HE'S SURE NOT GOING TO *LIKE* WHAT I HAVE TO TELL HIM!

TO ADMIRAL WILLIAM BLACKBIRD'S EYES, THE FLASH IS *MOMENTARY*.

THAT'S BECAUSE THEY HAVE ONLY A MILLISECOND TO RECORD THE BRIGHTER-THAN-NORMAL BRIGHTNESS OF THE LOW-WATT BULB BEFORE BEING COOKED INTO UNSEEING RAISINS.

IN REALITY, THE LIGHT CONTINUES TO FLARE LONG AFTER THE ADMIRAL LITERALLY OPENED THE DOOR ON HELL. THE EXPLOSION SHATTERS WINDOWS ALL THROUGH THE WEST WING OF THE WHITE HOUSE.

BAR-ROOM

FOLCROFT SANITARIUM, NERVE CENTER FOR THE *CURE.* THE OFFICE OF DR. HAROLD W. SMITH.

YES, MR. PRESIDENT, I CONCUR WITH YOUR ASSESSMENT. I'LL HAVE MY PEOPLE LOOK INTO IT AT ONCE.

SET UP YEARS AGO BY A NOW-DEAD PRESIDENT, CURE EXISTS TO METE OUT JUSTICE OUTSIDE OF NORMAL CONSTITUTIONAL RESTRICTIONS. OFFICIALLY, IT DOESN'T EXIST. BUT ONLY FIVE PEOPLE IN THE WORLD KNOW THAT—

THE PENTAGON'S PROBLEM IS NOW *CURE'S* PROBLEM, MacCLEARY.

I'LL GO WAKE UP REMO.

HE'S GONNA *LOVE* THIS ONE.

RISE AND SHINE, WILLIAMS. TIME TO SERVE YOUR UNGRATEFUL COUNTRY.

WHAT THE--??

DAMN! HE ESCAPED AGAIN.

GREAT. MacCLEARY FELL FOR IT!

100

HIS NAME IS *REMO*...

TIME TO MAKE MY MOVE.

ONCE HE WAS A NEWARK COP. HE LIVED AN ORDINARY LIFE UNTIL HE FOUND HIMSELF STRAPPED TO THE ELECTRIC CHAIR FOR A MURDER HE DIDN'T COMMIT. THE SWITCH WAS PULLED, AND REMO WOKE UP WITH A NEW FACE AND VERY FEW OPTIONS IN LIFE...

I ALWAYS SUSPECTED THAT IRISH S.O.B. WASN'T AS BRIGHT AS HE SEEMED.

OFFICIALLY, HE DOESN'T EXIST EITHER. WHEN HIS TRAINING IS COMPLETE, HE WILL BE *CURE'S* SOLE ENFORCEMENT ARM. UNLESS HE MANAGES TO ESCAPE FIRST...

SO FAR, HIS TRACK RECORD IS *NOT* GOOD...

WHAT DID I SNAG... A NAIL?

I WAS HALF WAY OUT THE BUILDING WHEN I REALIZED WE BUILT THAT WINDOW TOO SMALL FOR YOU TO SLIP THROUGH-

THE BARS ARE JUST TO SAVE YOU THE EMBARRASS-MENT OF GETTING *STUCK!*

YOU'VE GOT TO *HELP* ME, MacCLEARY! HE'S TRYING TO *KILL* ME!

WHO, *CHIUN?* THAT'S HIS JOB. IF YOU DON'T MAKE IT THROUGH TRAINING, YOU WON'T MAKE IT OUT IN THE FIELD! YOU GOT TO BE BADDER AND BALLSIER THAN ANY-ONE WE THROW YOU UP AGAINST.

I MEAN HE'S *REALLY* TRYING TO KILL ME! LOOK AT THIS. EVERYTIME I PUT ON A NEW SHIRT, HE PAINTS A *BULLSEYE* ON IT!

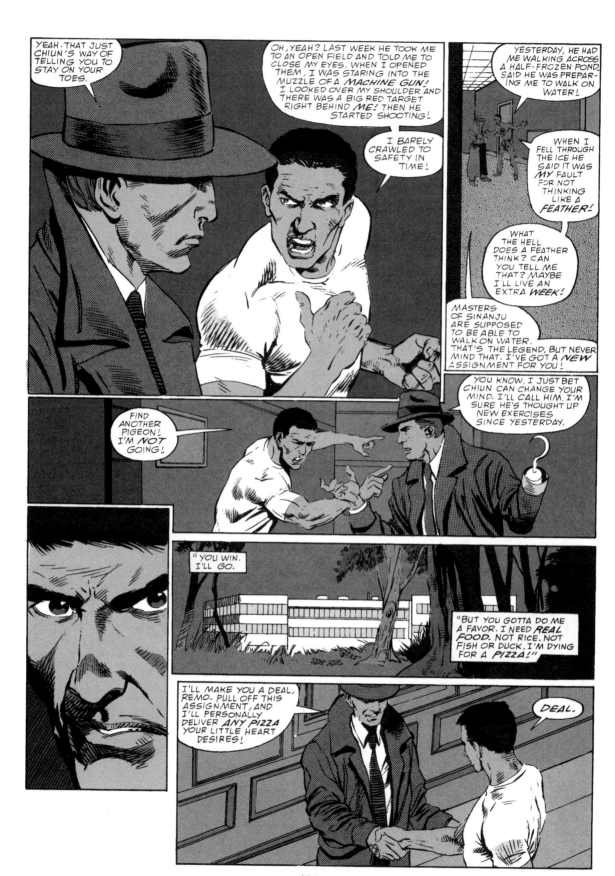

LET ME LAY IT OUT FOR YOU. THERE'S BEEN AN OUTBREAK OF SUSPICIOUS DEATHS AT THE PENTAGON. CLERKS FALLING DOWN STAIRS OR GETTING MANGLED BY ESCALATOR MACHINERY. ONE GUY HAD A WATER COOLER FALL ON HIM AND CRUSH HIS SKULL LIKE AN EGG.

LOOK AT CHIUN GIVING ME THE HAIRY EYEBALL. THE CRAFTY OLD REPROBATE. PRETENDING TO BE TRAINING ME WHEN ALL ALONG HE'S JUST TRYING TO *KILL* ME SO HE CAN GO BACK TO KOREA WITH THE FORTUNE MAC IS PAYING HIM.

IT LOOKED LIKE A RASH OF *FREAK ACCIDENTS* UNTIL ADMIRAL BLACKBIRD, CHAIRMAN OF THE JOINT CHIEFS OF STAFF, WAS KILLED WHEN HIS LIMO EXPLODED. HE WAS ABOUT TO HAND-DELIVER AN OFFICIAL REPORT ON THESE ACCIDENTS TO THE WHITE HOUSE.

WHAT DID THE REPORT SAY?

REMO IS IGNORING ME. VERY WELL, I WILL IGNORE *HIM*!

THIS IS WHERE IT GETS INTERESTING. THE REPORT WENT UP WITH THE LIMO. NO ONE CAN FIND THE OFFICE COPY. ADMIRAL BLACKBIRD'S AIDE, LT. LATHAM, HAD CUSTODY OF IT. THIS MORNING, HE MANAGED TO CUT HIS WRIST OPEN TRYING TO CLOSE A STUBBORN WINDOW.

HE BLED TO DEATH BEFORE ANYONE GOT TO HIM.

WHAT IMPERTINENCE! NOW HE IS IGNORING THE FACT THAT I AM IGNORING HIM.

THE PRESIDENT THINKS IT'S FOUL PLAY. WE HAVE ONLY ONE CLUE. *THIS.* IT WAS FOUND IN THE PENTAGON, NEAR BLACKBIRD'S PARKING SPACE.

I WILL SHOW HIM. I WILL IGNORE HIM TWICE AS CALLOUSLY AS HE IS IGNORING ME. AFTER A YEAR OR TWO HE WILL *BEG* ME TO SPEAK TO HIM. BUT I WILL NEVER RELENT. I WILL BE AS SILENT AS A STONE. HE WILL BE FOREVER DEPRIVED OF MY WISDOM!

THIS BABY'S SO SHARP IT'LL TAKE YOUR HAND OFF IF YOU PICK IT UP WRONG.

SO WHAT IS IT? A MASOCHIST'S BUTTONIERE?

SILENCE, IGNORANT WHITE THING! ANY IDIOT CAN SEE THAT IT IS A *SHURIKEN.*

A WHAT?

A NINJA THROWING STAR. THEY ARE USED TO DISCOURAGE PURSUERS. SOMETIMES TO DISTRACT THEM. NINJAS ARE VERY SNEAKY. I AM SURPRISED TO LEARN THEY PLAGUE THIS FARAWAY LAND.

NINJAS, HUH? CAN YOU HANDLE THEM?

OF COURSE. THEY ARE *JAPANESE*. EVERYBODY KNOWS THE LOWLY JAPANESE ARE *INFERIOR* TO WONDERFUL *KOREANS*.

NOT THAT *ALL* KOREANS ARE WONDERFUL. THOSE WHO DWELL SOUTH OF THE 38th PARALLEL ARE GREEDY AND EAT DOG. THOSE WHO LIVE JUST BEYOND MY HOME VILLAGE ARE UNCOUTH. EVEN AMONG MY VILLAGE SOME ARE LESS THAN PERFECT. I KNOW YOU FIND THIS DIFFICULT TO ACCEPT, BUT--

NEVER MIND, MASTER CHIUN. YOU AND REMO TRACK DOWN THIS NINJA AND *ELIMINATE* HIM.

REMO WILL NOT NEED ME.

DIDN'T YOU JUST CALL HIM *WORTHLESS*? YOU ONCE TOLD ME HE WAS AS UNTRAINABLE AS A *BABOON!*

IN FACT, YOU ASKED IF WE'D CONSIDER *REPLACING* HIM WITH A BABOON!

YOU SAID *THAT* ABOUT *ME*?!

STAY OUT OF THIS, WILLIAMS. WHAT ABOUT IT, CHIUN? IS HE UP TO THE JOB, OR NOT?

REMO *IS* WORTHLESS. BUT EVEN A WHITE CAN HANDLE A MERE NINJA.

THAT WILL TEACH HIM TO TREAT THE MASTER OF SINANJU LIKE A COMMON LIGHT POST.

WELL, THAT SOLVES ONE PROBLEM, ANYWAY...

YEAH? WHAT'S *THAT*?

WE CAN GET *YOU* INTO THE PENTAGON WITH A UNIFORM AND ID. BUT CHIUN WAS GOING TO BE A REAL CHALLENGE. HE ONLY WEARS *KIMONOS*.

THE PENTAGON LOADING DOCKS...

THERE YOU GO. SIX FILE CABINETS ORDERED AND SIX DELIVERED.

THIS WOULD'VE BEEN A LOT EASIER ON MY BACK IF YOU HAD A TWO WHEELER.

T.HAVEY

SORRY.

TRUCK DRIVERS. THEY'RE ALL ALIKE. LET THEM GET THEIR HANDS ON SOMETHING, AND YOU'LL NEVER SEE IT AGAIN!

BOY, THIS SUCKER IS *HEAVY.* ALL THIS WORK BECAUSE SOME JERK LIEUTENANT SLASHES HIS WRISTS AND NOBODY CAN FIND THE KEYS TO HIS OFFICE FILES. YOU'D THINK THE BRASS WOULD CALL A LOCKSMITH - BUT THAT WOULD BE *INTELLIGENT.* NO WONDER MY TAXES ARE SO HIGH.

THIS PLACE IS *RIDICULOUS!* YOU NEED A TREASURE MAP TO FIND THE MEN'S ROOM. IF I DON'T FIND WHAT I'M LOOKING FOR *SOON,* I'LL--

SPOKE TOO SOON. THERE IT IS.

ACCORDING TO MacCLEARY, LATHAM WAS ADMIRAL BLACK-BIRD'S AIDE. THERE COULD BE SOME CLUE TO WHAT THE MISSING REPORT WOULD HAVE SAID IN HIS FILES.

LIEUTENANT L.LATHAM

GREAT! UNLOCKED AND EMPTY! THIS MAY BE A QUICK IN-AND-OUT ASSIGNMENT.

108

NINJA... GOT... AWAY...

ARE YOU ALL RIGHT, SIR?

WHAT'D HE SAY?

SOUNDED LIKE "LINDA" MUST BE HIS GIRL-FRIEND.

HE'S OUT OF IT. C'MON, LET'S GRAB SOME FIRE EXTINGUISHERS WHILE WE CAN STILL GET THIS UNDER CONTROL!

Uhhhh... HURT ALL OVER. GOTTA MAKE MYSELF SCARCE BEFORE THEY COME BACK!

THEN I'M GONNA NAIL THAT LITTLE NINJA SNEAK IF I HAVE TO WALK EVERY INCH OF THIS RAT'S MAZE!

IT IS NIGHT. THEY ONLY COME OUT AT NIGHT.

FROM EVERY CRACK AND CREVICE,

DROPPING FROM THE CEILINGS.

SLITHERING OUT OF AIR DUCTS.

THEY EMERGE, THEIR BUG-BLACK EYES SHIFTING AND EVER WATCHFUL...

OBSERVE ONE NOW. THIS SPECIMEN IS LARGER THAN MOST. HE IS THE *JONIN*, OR LEADER OF HIS KIND...

HE IS BRED TO MOVE SILENTLY...

PAUSING ONLY TO RECONNOITER...

THEN, EMERGING WHEN HIS KEEN INTELLIGENCE PERCEIVES THAT NO ENEMIES LURK ABOUT...

SPLOOSH GURGLE

BEHOLD HIM. HE IS A *NINJA*. HE IS CUNNING PERSONIFIED.

TRAINED TO LIVE OFF THE HARSHEST OF ENVIRONMENTS, HE CAN EXIST FOR DAYS WITHOUT SUSTENANCE.

ALTHOUGH HUNGRY, HE FASTS WITHOUT COMPLAINT.

ALTHOUGH PARCHED, HE BRAVELY BIDES HIS TIME UNTIL HE CAN SLAKE HIS THIRST IN SAFETY.

KLUNK

THE NINJA IS RENOWNED FOR HIS AGILITY.

KLUNK

FAMED FOR HIS PERSISTENCE.

LEGENDARY FOR HIS ADAPTABILITY.

HARDSHIP AND OPPORTUNITY ARE AS ONE TO HIS CRAFTY MIND.

THE COURAGE OF THE NINJA IS UN-QUESTIONED. HE FEARS NOTHING, QUAILS BEFORE NO CHALLENGE-- NO MATTER HOW DAUNTING...

SLURP

YET HE WILL ALSO STOOP TO ANY LOW DEVICE IN ORDER TO ACCOMPLISH HIS EXHALTED MISSION.

NO MATTER THE TASK, HE ALWAYS SUCCEEDS...

FOR HE IS NINJA!

THE LOWER BASEMENT OF THE PENTAGON...

CONGRATULATIONS! YOU HAVE ALL SUCCESS-FULLY PENETRATED THIS FORTIFICATION. NOW WE WILL STRIKE IN NUMBERS.

LET THE AMERICAN MILITARY QUAKE IN TERROR--AS THE CITIZENS OF TRIPOLI DID WHEN THE U.S. STRUCK SO MERCILESSLY--

WHEN WILL THE LIBYAN LEADER PAY US OUR NEXT INSTALL-MENT?

SOON, MY GENIN. YOU HAVE BEEN SAVING YOUR RECEIPTS?

YES, JONIN. WE THROW OUT NOTHING.

GOOD. FOR THE LIBYAN COLONEL HAS PROMISED TO RE-IMBURSE US FOR ALL EXPENSES. INCLUDING GAS MILEAGE.

ONCE WE HAVE DEMONSTRATED TO THE WORLD THAT THE U.S. MILITARY IS NOT SAFE WITHIN ITS OWN HEADQUARTERS, WE WILL ESCAPE TO MEXICO AND MEET OUR LIBYAN PAYMASTER.

112

THEY ARE NINJA...

THEY FEAR NO FOE.

SHRINK FROM NO ODDS.

AND STOP AT NOTHING TO ACHIEVE THEIR ENDS.

THUD

COME. LET US RETURN TO OUR LAIRS BEFORE HIS BODY IS DISCOVERED. WE MEET AGAIN ONE HOUR BEFORE DAWN.

DOES ANYONE HAVE ANY CHOCOLATE LEFT? I CONSUMED MY LAST BAR.

WELL DONE. AND THESE BOXES WILL MAKE HIS DEATH LOOK ACCIDENTAL.

Uhhhh... WHERE AM I?

WALTER REED ARMY HOSPITAL. YOU *WERE* UNDER A PILE OF BOXES. YOU'RE DAMNED LUCKY THEY WERE FILLED WITH JUST TONGUE DEPRESSORS, AND NOT ORDNANCE.

NICE GOING, WILLIAMS-- YOU SCREWED UP BIG-- EVEN FOR YOU! CARE TO FILL US IN ON THE EMBARRASSING DETAILS?

THE PLACE IS INFESTED WITH THEM. THEY COME OUT OF THE FILING CABINETS AT NIGHT. HIDING IN THE MEN'S ROOM. THEY'VE GOTTEN AT THE CEILING FIXTURES.

HE'S BABBLING ABOUT COCK-ROACHES. HE MUST BE DELIRIOUS.

NO. HE IS DESCRIBING NINJAS. THEY ARE LIKE HUMAN COCK-ROACHES. NOT AS CLEAN OR INTELLIGENT.

LEAVE US, MacCLEARY. THIS IS BETWEEN MY PUPIL AND MYSELF.

OKAY. BUT IF THE PENTAGON SITUATION IS AS BAD AS REMO SAYS, WE HAVE TO FUMIGATE FAST.

I'LL BE OUTSIDE.

YOU HAVE SHAMED ME, PALE PIECE OF PIG'S EAR.

YOU SEND ME ON MY MERRY WAY TO BE BEATEN TO A PULP, AND YOU FEEL SHAME?

AND WHAT THE HELL IS A PALE PIECE OF PIG'S EAR?!

YOU ARE.

HOW MANY NINJAS DID YOU ENCOUNTER?

SIX OR SEVEN. BUT WHO CARES! I WAS OUT-NUMBERED!

EVEN ONE AS CLUMSY AND INEPT AS YOU SHOULD HAVE BEEN ABLE TO HANDLE A MERE SEVEN NINJAS!

I HAD A --ER-- LITTLE TROUBLE BEFOREHAND, OKAY?

I KNOW HOW THIS IS GOING TO SOUND, BUT I SAW ONE NINJA SCOOT OUT OF A FILE CABINET AND CHANGE A LIGHT-BULB.

114

WHEN I TRIED THE SWITCH, THE ROOM *EXPLODED.* I WASN'T TOO STEADY ON MY FEET AFTER THAT--

HOW WHITE OF YOU-- TO BLAME YOUR INEPTITUDE ON YOUR INNATE STUPIDITY. NINJAS FEAR PERSONAL *COMBAT.* SO THEY SNEAK ABOUT SETTING TRAPS. EXPLODING LIGHT-BULBS ARE JUST LIKE THEM--

BUT DIDN'T YOU TELL ME THEY'RE PUSHOVERS?

"AND I SPOKE TRULY. I, WHO AM MORE THAN TWICE YOUR AGE, COULD HAVE BEATEN ALL SEVEN WITH ONE HAND BEHIND MY BACK--"

"SURE, CHIUN, SURE."

"IT IS TRUE. I COULD HAVE DESTROYED THEM WITHOUT EVEN DEIGNING TO TOUCH THEM--"

IMPOSSIBLE! THEY WERE TOUGH. *REAL* TOUGH. YOU TALK A PRETTY GOOD FIGHT. BUT THESE GUYS HAD SWORDS, NUNCHUCKS, AND ALL THAT BRUCE LEE STUFF.

A *PITIFUL* EXCUSE IF I EVER HEARD ONE. THEY WERE ENCUMBERED WITH JUNK AND YOUR HANDS WERE FREE TO STRIKE CLEAN BLOWS AND STILL YOU ALLOWED THEM TO DEFEAT YOU.

I AM REMINDED OF AN ANCIENT KOREAN JOKE WHICH ASKS, "HOW MANY NINJAS DOES IT TAKE TO SCREW UP A LIGHT BULB?"

IN. YOU MEAN SCREW *IN.* NOT UP. GET IT RIGHT.

YOU OBVIOUSLY DO NOT KNOW NINJAS VERY WELL. TONIGHT YOU WILL REST. I WILL TELL MACCLEARY THAT YOU WILL BE PREPARED TO DESTROY THESE NINJAS TO-MORROW.

ARE YOU *CRAZY?!* I CAN BARELY WALK! THOSE GUYS ARE KILL-ING PEOPLE! THIS CAN'T WAIT FOR A GRUDGE REMATCH!

SUCH TRIVIA IS OF NO CONSEQUENCE TO ME. WHAT TRULY MATTERS IS *HONOR.* I HAVE STOOPED TO TRAINING YOU--A MERE WHITE-- IN THE GLORIOUS ART OF SINANJU. AND YOU HAVE DISGRACED ME BY FAILING TO BEST THESE SKULKING THIEVES!

THE PITIFUL GAME THEY CALL NINJUTSU-- THE SO-CALLED ART OF STEALTH-- IT IS ACTUALLY THE ART OF *STEALING.* ALL OF THEIR TRICKS WERE STOLEN FROM EARLY MASTERS OF SINANJU!

THIEVES?

THIS WAS IN THE DAYS BEFORE THE GREAT MASTER WANG, WHEN MASTERS OF SINANJU CARRIED WEAPONS, OF COURSE.

THAT IS WHY NINJAS GO ABOUT WITH THEIR FACES COVERED. IT IS A CURSE AN EARLY MASTER PLACED ON THEIR HEADS TO REMIND THEM OF THEIR SHAMELESS BEGINNINGS!

WHAT?! NO MASK?!

SOME- ONE SHOULD CLUE IN THE HEAD NINJA. HE DIDN'T WEAR ANY MASK!

THIS IS AN *OUTRAGE!* THE HOUSE OF SINANJU TOLERATES NINJAS ONLY BECAUSE THEY DEMON- STRATE OUR SUPERIORITY!!

COME! I MUST PUT A *STOP* TO THIS!

WE ARE GOING TO THE PENTAGRAM!

POP

IT'S THE PENTA*GON.* AND-- OOWWW!

BE CAREFUL! I KNOW HE'S NOT MUCH, BUT REMO'S THE ONLY ENFORCEMENT ARM CURE HAS!

MacCLEARY! INFORM YOUR PRESIDENT THAT THESE NINJAS WILL NOT WITNESS ANOTHER SUNRISE.

WE MAY BE ABLE TO SALVAGE HIM!

WHY DO THESE CONVEYANCES NOT STOP FOR US?

IT'S AN AMERICAN TRADITION. LIKE BEING MUGGED.

WE HAVE TO WAIT FOR A FREE ONE TO COME ALONG.

I HAVE NO TIME TO WASTE.

KRAK

KLANK

TO THE PENTAGRAM, O FORTUNATE DRIVER.

HE MEANS PENTAGON.

AND THERE WILL BE A FAT TIP IF YOU GET US THERE FAST.

DID YOU GUYS SEE THAT?

THAT LIGHT POST FELL OVER FOR NO REASON.

THIS IS EXACTLY WHAT HAPPENED IN THE FINAL DAYS OF THE ROMAN EMPIRE.

AMERICA TRULY IS IN DECLINE.

GET SERIOUS, CHIUN. ROME DIDN'T HAVE LIGHT POSTS. AND I HAVE MY DOUBTS ABOUT LIGHTBULBS IN ANCIENT KOREA.

I WAS MERELY *CALMING* THE DRIVER.

AS FOR MY RIDDLE, I TOLD YOU THE *MODERN* VERSION.

THE ORIGINAL ASKS "HOW MANY NINJAS DOES IT TAKE TO LIGHT A CANDLE?"

SO WHAT'S THE ANSWER?

THINK ABOUT IT. WHEN YOU SEE THE NINJAS FOR WHAT THEY TRULY ARE, WISDOM WILL COME TO YOU.

ALTHOUGH I DOUBT IT.

THIS IS AS FAR AS I CAN TAKE YOU- ONLY OFFICIAL VEHICLES BEYOND THIS POINT-

HEY! WHAT ABOUT MY TIP ??

BEWARE LIGHTPOSTS. EVERYWHERE I GO, THEY ARE FALLING LIKE OLD BAMBOO.

"HOW DO WE GET IN, CHIUN? BETWEEN MY PAJAMAS AND YOUR KIMONO, WE'RE KINDA CONSPICUOUS."

"LEAVE THAT TO ME."

UHHHH...

THE GUARD SLEEPS. HIS UNIFORM SHOULD FIT YOU.

YOU GOTTA BE KIDDING! THAT GUY HAD TWENTY POUNDS ON ME.

I HATE TO BRING THIS UP AT A TIME LIKE THIS, BUT I THINK THE PENTAGON GUARDS SHOOT-ON-SIGHT.

IF YOU ARE SHOT, DO NOT EXPECT ME TO CARRY YOU.

PERISH FORBID.

LEAD ME TO THE PLACE THE NINJAS CONCEAL THEMSELVES.

DOWN THIS CORRIDOR.

THIS IS THE ONE. BUT THEY HAVE REPLACED THE DOOR. IT'S LOCKED.

STEP ASIDE.

CAN I LOAN YOU A JIMMY OR A CREDIT CARD?

NO. THERE IS NO NEED TO BRIBE THE GUARD TO LET US IN. PROPER PRESSURE, CORRECTLY APPLIED--

THAK

--WILL DO.

SEE THAT FILE CABINET? HE CAME OUT OF THE TOP DRAWER.

COME OUT COME OUT WHERE EVER YOU ARE, NINJA.

RAP RAP RAP

Hmm. HE DOES NOT ANSWER.

MAYBE HE'S MOVED UP TO A BROOM CLOSET!

NONSENSE. THE NINJA IS A CREATURE OF HABIT.

HE ALWAYS RETURNS TO HIS LAIR—

ALSO, THEY SNORE.

I DETECT RUDE SOUNDS COMING FROM THIS CABINET.

SCREEE

HIS FINGERNAIL! IT'S GOING THROUGH THAT SHEET METAL LIKE A BAND-SAW!

CHECK IT OUT. HE'S NAPPING.

IN FEUDAL TIMES, THEY SLEPT IN HOLLOW TREE TRUNKS. AS A CONSEQUENCE, THEY WERE ALWAYS SCRATCHING THEMSELVES.

TERMITES.

121

NO WONDER YOUR POSTURE IS ATROCIOUS! YOU ARE BENT OVER WITH *JUNK!*

LOOK AT THIS PLACE. THEY COULD BE HIDING ANYWHERE!

HUSH. I HEAR VOICES.

HEEL, NINJA-

HOLD THIS CUR, REMO, WHILE I SEEK THE SOURCE OF THOSE VOICES.

ME? YOU WANT ME TO HOLD *HIM?*

THIS WILL TAKE BUT A MOMENT. I DETECT ONLY SIX VOICES.

SETTLE DOWN, YOU!

I SAID SETTLE *DOWN!*

BONK

IT IS THE APPOINTED HOUR. BUT WHAT IS KEEPING *SAKIMA?*

WHERE COULD HE BE?

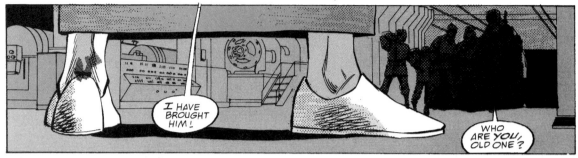

I HAVE BROUGHT HIM!

WHO ARE *YOU*, OLD ONE?

I AM *CHIUN*, MASTER OF SIN-ANJU--

PERHAPS YOU HAVE *HEARD* OF SINANJU?

OF COURSE. A FORGOTTEN FISHING VILLAGE NO ONE GOES TO ANYMORE. THERE HAS NOT BEEN A MASTER OF SINANJU IN A HUNDRED YEARS!

BASE *LIES!*

JUST WHAT I WOULD EXPECT FROM A THIEF WHO DOES NOT HONOR TRADITION BY COVERING HIS *FACE!*

THE CURSE OF SINANJU WAS LIFTED LONG AGO, OLD MAN. I WEAR NO MASK TO SHOW THIS TO THE WORLD.

MY FOLLOWERS WEAR THEIRS AS A SIGN OF FEALTY TO THEIR LEADER--

I SAY THAT I AM A TRUE MASTER OF SINANJU--

YE!!!

YAHH!

HAA!

AYAA!

--AND I CHALLENGE YOUR WHELPS, DOG IN A LONG LINE OF DOGS!!

TAKE HIM!

WATCH CAREFULLY, REMO, AND BEHOLD THE TRUE NATURE OF THE OVERRATED NINJA TRIBE!

CHIUN! DON'T JUST *STAND* THERE!

THEY'LL *SLAUGHTER* YOU!

GAKK!

THE NINJA IS ESPECIALLY FEARSOME WHEN HE ATTACKS EN MASS...

HA!!!

ZIIIIIZZZ

STAND CLEAR! HE IS MINE!

DIE!!

NO, I CLAIM HIM!!

TOO *SLOW*, NINJA.

LIKE ALL YOUR SCUTTLING ILK!

HE STRIKES WITHOUT HESITATION, WITHOUT FEAR...

IS THIS THE BEST YOU CAN DO??

SMAKK

UGH!

WHEN HIS BROTHER FAILS, ANOTHER TAKES HIS PLACE...

UNTIL VICTORY IS WITHIN REACH--

I HAVE ENJOYED THIS, FOR I AM FRAIL AND GET SO LITTLE EXERCISE.

THE NINJA ENCIRCLES HIS DOOMED AND HELPLESS VICTIM.

YAAHH!

BUT NOW I MUST CATCH MY BREATH.

HI'IEE!

STRIKING IN FULL CRY.

YEEOWP!

UNFAZED BY OBSTACLES.

UNDAUNTED BY MISCALCULATION.

GAAH!

RIDICULOUS IN VICTORY...

MAGNIFICENT IN DEFEAT.

YOU SEE, REMO? THEY ARE OVER-PRAISED.

GURGLE

129

130

THE TRUE ANSWER IS: "NONE." NINJAS ARE AFRAID TO LIGHT CANDLES, FOR EVEN CANDLE-LIGHT EXPOSES THEIR INCOMPETENCE FOR ALL TO SEE.

IS THAT THE PUNCH LINE?

AM I SUPPOSED TO LAUGH OR SOMETHING?

I MUST TELL MacCLEARY TO ADD THE LACK OF A SENSE OF HUMOR TO THE GROWING LIST OF YOUR MANY DEFICIENCIES...

HERE YOU GO, KID! A GUIDO CHANG SPECIAL!

WITH EXTRA MONOSODIUM GLUTAMATE.

OH BOY! MY FAVORITE! CHINESE PIZZA!

NEVER HEARD OF SUCH A THING MYSELF!

IT'S THE LATEST THING! IT'S GOT A RICE CRUST AND 37 AUTHENTIC ORIENTAL INGREDIENTS. BEAN SPROUTS, WATER CHESNUTS, THE WORKS!

WHAT'S THAT ON TOP-- A PAIR OF CHOPSTICKS?

NOPE.

IT'S THE SPARE RIB GARNISH!

I *HATE* BROWN RICE!

TOUGH BREAK, KID.

BUT THAT'S THE WAY IT GOES SOME DAYS...

WHAT ABOUT OUR DEAL? I HELD UP MY PART OF THE BARGAIN!

AND I HELD UP MINE- YOU GOT THE PIZZA!

BUT I DIDN'T PROMISE THAT YOU'D GET TO *EAT* IT, NOW DID I?

YOU SET ME UP *AGAIN,* YOU BASTARD!

KLANGG

LAUGH WHILE YOU CAN, MacCLEARY! SOME DAY I'LL HAVE THE LAST LAUGH...

SOME DAY...

END

TALES OF SINANJU
"HOW THE THIEVING NINJA CAME TO BE"

YOU ARE PRIVILEGED TONIGHT, REMO, FOR I WILL NOW READ TO YOU FROM THE SCROLLS OF MY ANCESTOR, *MASTER SAM.* PERHAPS YOU HAVE HEARD OF HIM?

OH, SURE. EVERYBODY KNOWS *SAM.* I HEAR HIS NAME *ALL* THE TIME.

WHAT THE HELL AM I DOING HERE? BESIDES DYING OF *BOREDOM.*

TV GUIDE

SOAP OPERA DIGEST

I AM PLEASED THAT HIS FAME HAS SPREAD TO EVEN THIS UNENLIGHTENED *BACK-WATER.*

NOW THIS TALE IS INSCRIBED IN THE BOOK OF SINANJU AS "HOW THE THIEVING NINJA CAME TO BE."

WONDERFUL. I LET A BUNCH OF *NINJAS* BEAT THE STUFFING OUT OF ME AND AS *PUNISHMENT* I HAVE TO LISTEN TO KOREAN FAIRY TALES.

IN THE YEAR 1282 AD BY WESTERN DATING AND OUR YEAR OF THE DOG, AN EMPEROR OF JAPAN HIRED MASTER SAM TO DISPATCH A PLOTTER WHO THREATENED THE CHRYSANTHEMUM THRONE.

MASTER SAM JOURNEYED TO KYOTO AND WAS TOLD BY THE EMPEROR THAT THIS ENEMY WOULD BE AT SUCH AND SUCH A PLACE AT A CERTAIN TIME.

SAM LAY IN WAIT, AND WHEN THE PLOTTER APPEARED, HE SWOOPED DOWN ON HIM--AND THE PLOTTER WAS NO MORE.

RETURNING TO THE EMPEROR, MASTER SAM WAS RECEIVED IN GRATITUDE AND WAS INFORMED THAT ANOTHER BASE PLOTTER HAD BEEN DISCOVERED.

HEEDING THE EMPEROR'S INSTRUCTIONS, MASTER SAM SLEW THIS ONE WITH A SINGLE BLOW.

YET WHEN MASTER SAM RETURNED TO THE EMPEROR TO RECEIVE HIS PAYMENT, HE WAS TOLD THAT STILL MORE ENEMIES HAD BEEN UNCOVERED.

THE DETAILS OF MASTER SAM'S METHODS OF DEALING WITH THESE ENEMIES ARE UNIMPORTANT. BUT THEY SHOWED THE EMPEROR'S SUBJECTS THE FOLLY OF THREATENING TO HARM HIM.

YET STILL ENEMIES CONTINUED TO VEX THE JAPANESE EMPEROR. AND MASTER SAM GREW SUSPICIOUS.

ARRIVING EARLY AT THE PLACE WHERE A SIXTH PLOTTER WAS SUPPOSED TO BE LURKING, MASTER SAM DISCOVERED A SPY IN HIDING.

AND MASTER SAM FELLED THIS SPY WITH A HARSH BLOW TO THE NECK AND DEMANDED OF HIM, "WHY DO YOU SPY UPON THE MASTER OF SINANJU, DOG OF THE EMPEROR?"

AND THE SPY REPLIED IN AN ABJECT VOICE, "O, MASTER, MY EMPEROR SEEKS THE SECRETS OF SINANJU, WHICH I HAVE BEEN OBSERVING." AND THE WRETCH REVEALED THAT THE EMPEROR HAD NO ENEMIES, FOR SAM HAD BEEN KILLING INNOCENT PEASANTS.

HEARING THIS, MASTER SAM ASKED THE SPY, "WHAT HAVE YOU LEARNED OF SINANJU?"

AND THE SPY TOLD HOW HE HAD LEARNED HOW TO MOVE STEALTHILY WEARING THE COLORS OF NIGHT, HOW TO CLIMB WALLS LIKE A SPIDER, AND CERTAIN LETHAL OPEN-HANDED BLOWS.

AND THE MASTER ASKED THAT HE SHOW HIM. WHEREUPON, THE SPY BEGAN TO CLIMB A BAMBOO FENCE.

BUT HE SLIPPED, REVEALING SPIKED TOOLS ON HIS HANDS AND FEET WHICH HE USED TO ACCOMPLISH WHAT SINANJU DID BY HAND.

AND SEEING THIS, MASTER SAM SCOLDED THE SPY, SAYING, "RETURN TO YOUR EMPEROR AND TELL HIM THE MASTER OF SINANJU KILLS FOR PAYMENT --NOT FOR THE ENLIGHTENMENT OF EMPERORS."

I DON'T GET IT, CHIUN. HOW COME SAM DIDN'T JUST *KILL* THE SPY?

HE WAS NOT PAID TO KILL SPIES--ONLY *PEASANTS*.

WELL, THAT WAS A REALLY *FASCINATING* STORY--

WHICH IS NOT YET OVER. *SIT!*

MANY YEARS LATER, WORD CAME OUT OF JAPAN OF A NEW SECT OF ASSASSINS WHO DRESSED IN BLACK AND WERE KNOWN AS THE *NINJA*. AND MASTER SAM, NOW OLDER, JOURNEYED UNHERALDED TO JAPAN TO SEE THESE NINJA WITH HIS OWN EYES.

HE FOUND A SMALL BAND OF THEM, LIVING IN ROUGH WOODS.

THEY WERE LED BY THE UNIMPORTANT SPY OF YEARS BEFORE, WHO HAD TRAINED THEM. AND ALTHOUGH THEY WERE AS CLUMSY AS MONKEYS, THEY HAD TAKEN WORK THAT BELONGED TO SINANJU.

MASTER SAM STEPPED BEFORE THIS THIEF OF A SPY AND HIS FACE WAS WRATHFUL. AND THE NINJA, RECOGNIZING A SUPERIOR BEING, SHRANK FROM HIS STEELY GAZE.

AND MASTER SAM SAID TO HIM, "YOU HAVE STOLEN THAT WHICH LASTS LONGER THAN RUBIES. YOU HAVE STOLEN WISDOM. I COULD KILL YOU, NINJA, BUT YOU ARE BUT A CHILD IMITATING HIS ELDERS. INSTEAD, I CURSE YOU, AND ALL WHO FOLLOW YOUR PATH, TO FOREVER-MORE CONCEAL YOUR FACES IN SHAME."

"AND SHOULD ANY NINJA PERFORM HIS WORK WITH HIS FACE UNCOVERED," MASTER SAM WARNED, "THE MASTER OF SINANJU WILL NO LONGER SUFFER YOUR EXISTENCE."

AND THAT, REMO, IS WHY TO THIS VERY DAY THE SO-CALLED NINJA GO ABOUT WITH THEIR FACES MASKED BY CLOTH.

THAT EXPLAINS WHY YOU WERE SO *UPSET* WITH THAT NINJA WE TANGLED WITH LAST WEEK. BUT I STILL *DON'T* UNDERSTAND WHY SAM DIDN'T JUST KILL THOSE DIPPY NINJAS.

ARE YOU *DEAF?* I EXPLAINED THAT. HE WAS NOT *PAID.*

AN ASSASSIN *DOES NOT KILL,* EXCEPT FOR GOLD. SOMETIMES FOR REASONS OF *HONOR.*

BUT NOT KILLING THEM TOOK *WORK* FROM YOUR ANCESTORS.

WOULDN'T IT HAVE BEEN *SMARTER* TO WIPE THEM OUT AND BE DONE WITH IT?

NO!

IT WOULD HAVE BEEN SMARTER HAD I NOT *WASTED* MY PRECIOUS TALE ON ONE SUCH AS YOURSELF! *BEGONE!*

WHAT'S YOUR PROBLEM? IT WAS A LEGITIMATE QUESTION.

WHICH PROVES THAT YOU HAVE LEARNED *NOTHING.* NOW GO-- AND DO NOT RETURN UNTIL YOU ARE PREPARED TO THINK UPON THESE PEARLS OF WISDOM I SET BEFORE YOU, PALE PIECE OF PIG'S EAR.

NO SWEAT, PAL. YOU COULDN'T *BRIBE* ME TO SIT STILL FOR ANOTHER OF YOUR SILLY CAMPFIRE STORIES.

END

140

MORE TALES OF THE SINANJU

"NOW IN TIMES PAST, MASTERS OF SINANJU WORKED FOR VARIOUS THRONES. WE WERE HONORED BY THE PEACOCK THRONE OF PERSIA, THE CHRYSANTHEMUM THRONE OF JAPAN AND THE DRAGON THRONE OF KOREA."

"IN AMERICA, THEY DO THINGS DIFFERENTLY. THE MAN WHO SITS ON THE EAGLE THRONE IN WASHINGTON IS CALLED THE PRESIDENT."

"LEST SOME MISTAKENLY SUGGEST THAT PRESIDENT IS AN AMERICAN WORD FOR EMPEROR, LIKE CALIPH OR DEY, I WILL NOW PUT THAT LIE TO REST."

"THE PRESIDENT DOES NOT RULE THIS NATION, ALTHOUGH MANY OF HIS SUPPOSED SUBJECTS BELIEVE THIS."

"IN TRUTH, HE IS SO UNIMPORTANT THAT HE IS ONLY ALLOWED TO OCCUPY THE WHITE HOUSE (YES, A MERE HOUSE, NOT A CASTLE) FOR BUT EIGHT YEARS. IN EXTREME CASES, FOUR."

"THIS IS A LINE OF RULERS WHICH, AMAZINGLY, DOES NOT PASS FROM FATHER TO SON."

"IT IS SO UNIMPORTANT THAT LITERALLY ANYONE CAN BECOME PRESIDENT, IF HE IS WILLING TO SQUANDER A FORTUNE IN PURSUIT OF THIS OFFICE."

"MANY LOW-BORN PERSONS HAVE BECOME PRESIDENT, INCLUDING CRASS LAWYERS."

"EVEN HUMBLE FARMERS HAVE ASPIRED TO THIS POSITION-- WITH THE INEVITABLE CONSEQUENCES."

"I AM TOLD THAT ONLY RECENTLY AN ACTOR, DISTRAUGHT OVER HIS FLAGGING CAREER, WAS REDUCED TO BECOMING A PRESIDENT."

"I SWEAR THAT THIS IS TRUE."

"IF FURTHER PROOF IS NEEDED OF THIS MINOR FUNCTIONARY'S LACK OF IMPORTANCE, LET IT BE KNOWN THAT EVEN THOUGH I HAVE WORKED FOR AMERICA FOR NEARLY A YEAR, I HAVE NEVER MET THIS LACKEY."

"NOR DO I WISH TO."

"AS UNIMPORTANT AS THIS MAN IS, THERE ARE OTHERS EVEN LESS IMPORTANT. THE AMERICANS HAVE A SENATE, WHICH THEY STOLE FROM THE ROMANS. THEY HAVE DEBASED THIS ODD CONCEPT EVEN FURTHER BY ADDING WHAT THEY CALL CONGRESSMEN. MANY OF THESE ARE CONVICTED FELONS."

"THEN THERE IS THE VICE-PRESIDENT, SO-CALLED BECAUSE HIS VICES ARE MULTITUDINOUS. ALTHOUGH HE RECEIVES A PRINCELY STIPEND FROM HIS SUBJECTS, HE DOES NO WORK AND MAKES NO DECISIONS--MERELY BIDING HIS TIME IN INDOLENCE, WAITING FOR THE PRESIDENT TO DIE."

"MOST PRESIDENTS DO NOT DIE, AND THE LOT OF THE PRESIDENT OF VICE IS NOT A PARTICULARLY UNHAPPY ONE."

"AMONG THE OTHERS WHO RUN THIS COUNTRY ARE A MILITARY TRIBUNAL WHOSE PURPOSE I DO NOT UNDERSTAND, BUT THEY ARE OBVIOUSLY IMPORTANT BECAUSE THEY HAVE THOSE MOST IMPRESSIVE TITLES."

"I REFER TO THE POSTMASTER GENERAL, THE SURGEON GENERAL, AND THE ATTORNEY GENERAL -- A TRIUMVERATE SO FEARSOME THAT AMERICA HAS STOOD UNINVADED FOR OVER A CENTURY."

"NOW WE COME TO THE TRUE RULER OF AMERICA."

"HIS NAME IS UNKNOWN TO MOST AMERICANS. MANY THINK OF HIM AS A MERE DOCTOR."

"HE IS DR. HAROLD W. SMITH."

"LEST ANY UNFAMILIAR WITH THE WAYS OF AMERICA THINK THIS FEARSOME POTENTATE IS A MERE MENDER OF BONES, THIS IS NOT TRUE, FOR HE ASSURES ME THAT HE IS NOT."

"THUS, EMPEROR SMITH, WHO WILL HENCEFORTH BE CHRONICLED AS HAROLD THE GENEROUS, HOLDS FORTH IN AN IMPRESSIVE CASTLE CALLED FOLCROFT SANITARIUM."

"THIS LAST WORD IS ONE SUBJECT TO MANY POSSIBLE TRANSLATIONS, ONE OF WHICH IS 'INSANE ASYLUM.' BUT BE ASSURED THAT IN THIS CONTEXT, IT MEANS FORTRESS."

"THUS EMPEROR SMITH RESIDES WITHIN FORTRESS FOLCROFT IS THE CORRECT USAGE. EMPLOY NO OTHER."

"NOW HAROLD THE GENEROUS IS A VERY WISE RULER, FOR HE IS THE FIRST AMERICAN RULER TO DISPLAY THE WISDOM TO HIRE A MASTER OF SINANJU TO GUARD HIS SHORES -- WHICH I DO, ASSISTED BY A WHITE SERVANT, WHOM I AM PRETENDING TO TRAIN IN THE ART OF SINANJU AS A DIVERSION."

"I BELIEVE THIS WHITE, WHO IS KNOWN AS REMO, MAY ONE DAY PERFORM THE FUNCTION OF COURT JESTER."

"NOW THIS EMPEROR, HAROLD THE GENEROUS, IS AN AMAZING PERSON TO BEHOLD."

"HE WEARS NO KINGLY ROBES, IS ATTENDED BY NO ENTOURAGE, YET THROUGH AN ORACLE CALLED THE COMPUTER, WHOSE MYSTERIES REMAIN UNKNOWN TO ME, HE COMMANDS MIGHTY ARMIES AND TAKES ORDERS FROM NO ONE, NOT EVEN THE SO-CALLED PRESIDENT."

"HE DOES NOT EVEN WEAR A CROWN BECAUSE--"

REMO! WHY DOES EMPEROR SMITH NOT WEAR A CROWN?

HOW MANY TIMES DO I HAVE TO TELL YOU?

BECAUSE HE'S NOT AN EMPEROR!

"BECAUSE AMERICA HAS MANY ENEMIES, AND THESE PLOTTERS CONSIDER THE PRESIDENT THEIR TRUE FOE. THIS ELABORATE SUBTERFUGE INSURES THAT IF THESE ENEMIES STRIKE, ONLY UNIMPORTANT PRESIDENTS WILL FALL."

HOW ABOUT BURGER TRIUMPH, THEN?

"ALL HAIL HAROLD THE GENEROUS! LONG MAY HE REIGN!"

147

THIS IS AN *OUTRAGE!* THERE IS NO *MENTION* OF SINANJU!

WHY *WOULD* THERE BE?

BECAUSE IT WAS *WE* WHO DISPATCHED THAT MISERABLE HOOD, ROBIN.

YOU'RE *NOT* SERIOUS?

ONE OF YOUR *ANCESTORS* ASSASSINATED ROBIN HOOD?

BUT HE'S ONE OF MY HEROES!

SIT!

WHILE I'M WAITING FOR MY BEAUTIFUL DRAMA, I WILL TELL YOU THE *TRUE* STORY OF YOUR "HERO."

THIS *BETTER* HAVE A GOOD ENDING -- NOT LIKE THAT STUPID *NINJA* STORY.

IT HAS A VERY *HAPPY* ENDING. LISTEN.

THIS SO-CALLED "HERO" WAS AN UNKEMPT BANDIT, NOT AT ALL LIKE THE PRETTY ENGLISH SONGS THAT TELL OF HIS EXPLOITS.

NOW THE KING OF ENGLAND, WISHING TO BE *RID* OF THIS BOTHERSOME POACHER, SENT FOR THE MASTER OF SINANJU, WHO WAS AT THAT TIME, CHEE.

HEARING THE SORRY CHARGES AGAINST ROBIN HOOD, THE MASTER SOUGHT HIM OUT IN THE FOREST CALLED *SHERWOOD*.

HE FOUND THIS ROBIN HOOD ILL AND IN BED. SO THE MASTER TOLD THE POACHER'S UNDERLINGS--CUTTHROATS ALL--THAT HE WAS A *HEALER*.

THEREUPON THEY BEGGED THE MASTER TO CURE ROBIN HOOD IN THE MANNER THEN IN USE IN THAT LAND--WHICH WAS TO DRAW THE POISONS FROM THE BLOOD USING LEECHES.

NOW THE MASTER CHEE KNEW THAT *LEECHING* A MAN WAS NONSENSE,

BUT HE DID AS ASKED AND BLED THE BANDIT.

WHEN, OF COURSE, THE BANDIT DID NOT RECOVER...

CHEE BLED HIM *AGAIN*.

WITH THE EXPECTED RESULTS.

THREE TIMES MASTER CHEE *BLED* ROBIN HOOD.

AND THE SICKER HE BECAME, THE MORE LEECHES HIS CUT-THROATS BROUGHT, ENTREATING THE MASTER OF SINANJU WITH *PITEOUS* CRIES TO *SAVE* THEIR DYING CHIEFTAIN.

AND SO DID ROBIN HOOD *PERISH*-- PALE AND WEAK AND UNAWARE THAT HE WAS BEING *DISPATCHED* BY THE GREATEST ASSASSIN OF THAT TIME.

WHEREUPON THE CUTTHROATS OF ROBIN HOOD FELL TO WEEPING. DESPITE THEIR SORROW, THEY GRACIOUSLY *PAID* THE MASTER A GOLD SHILLING IN RETURN FOR HIS *VALIANT* EFFORTS.

AND SO CHEE BADE THEM FAREWELL.

IS THAT NOT A *WONDERFUL* STORY, REMO?

WONDERFUL? IT'S AWFUL! YOUR ANCESTOR *MURDERED* ROBIN HOOD!

A *MINOR* POINT.

THE WONDERFUL-NESS IS THAT MASTER CHEE COLLECTED A *DOUBLE* FEE--ONE FROM THE KINDLY ENGLISH KING AND A SECOND FROM THE VICTIM'S OWN RAGTAG BAND.

IS *MONEY* ALL YOU CARE ABOUT?

NO. I *ALSO* CARE ABOUT MY BEAUTIFUL DRAMA.

NOW *GO*--IT IS TIME FOR *EDGE OF DARKNESS!*

GOOD. I'LL *SNEAK* DOWN TO THE PIZZA HUT.

DOCTOR-- WHAT IS IT?

YOUR TUMOR. IT'S *TERMINAL.* I'M SORRY.

SNIFF!

END.

NOW WHAT?

I *KNOW* IT IS IN HERE SOMEWHERE...

NICE MOVE, WILLIAMS.

SMACK!

NOW YOU HAVE TO LISTEN TO ANOTHER KOREAN TALL TALE.

AH!

THIS IS ONE OF THE *GREATEST* TREASURES OF SINANJU, REMO.

YOU ARE VERY PRIVILEGED FOR NO OUTSIDER HAS EVER BEFORE GAZED UPON WHAT I AM ABOUT TO REVEAL TO YOUR ASTOUNDED WHITE ORBS.

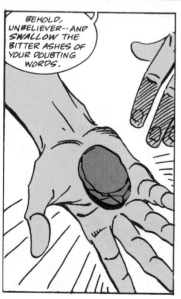

BEHOLD, UNBELIEVER--AND *SWALLOW* THE BITTER ASHES OF YOUR DOUBTING WORDS.

A ROCK?

152

NO, NO ORDINARY ROCK. IT IS A RARE STONE TAKEN FROM THE MOON.

THE MOON?

REALLY? DID *SMITH* GIVE IT TO YOU? IF ANYONE COULD HAVE...

OF COURSE NOT!

THIS STONE WAS *GIVEN* TO ME BY MY FATHER, WHO HAD IT FROM HIS FATHER, AND SO ON, BACK TO THE ONE WHO *PLUCKED* IT FROM THE VERY MOUNTAINS OF THE MOON--MASTER SHANG.

NEVER HEARD OF HIM!

HE IS THE MASTER WHO *WALKED* TO THE MOON.

WALKED! DID YOU SAY *WALKED*?

I DO NOT *BLAME* YOU FOR YOUR INCREDULITY, SHANG IS A LESSER-KNOWN MASTER--DESPITE BEING FIRST TO WALK TO THE MOON.

BULL! NEIL ARMSTRONG WAS THE FIRST, AND HE WALKED ON THE MOON, NOT *TO* IT!

NOT SO. LISTEN, AND I WILL TELL YOU THE TRUE TALE OF MASTER SHANG.

I KNOW SINANJU MASTERS CAN WALK ON WATER--

BUT TO THE MOON?

153

IT WAS IN THE TIME OF CHINA'S HAN DYNASTY. MASTER SHANG WAS THE MASTER IN THOSE DAYS. THIS WAS BEFORE THE GREAT WANG DISCOVERED THE SUN SOURCE, WHEN MASTERS OF SINANJU STILL CARRIED WEAPONS. SHANG WAS NOT A GREAT MASTER EXCEPT FOR THIS ONE FEAT, WHICH NO MASTER BEFORE OR SINCE HAS ACCOMPLISHED.

NOW MASTER SHANG OFTEN PERFORMED SERVICES FOR THE EMPEROR OF CHINA, IN THOSE DAYS, THE DRAGON THRONE WAS SORE BESET BY ENEMIES -- PRINCELINGS AND PRETENDERS WHO COVETED HIS GOLD AND WOMEN.

FOR THE EMPEROR HAD A QUEEN AND MANY CONCUBINES -- THIS BEING THE TRADITION AT THAT TIME.

OFTEN MASTER SHANG MADE THE ARDUOUS JOURNEY TO CHINA. AND EVERY TIME SHANG OBLITERATED AN ENEMY, MORE WOULD SPRING UP.

FOR EVERY ENEMY HAD FRIENDS AND RELATIVES, WHO TOOK UP THEIR CAUSE.

ONE DAY, SHANG SAID TO THE EMPEROR, "LO, YOUR ENEMIES WAX LIKE THE STARS AT NIGHT. EACH YEAR I AM SUMMONED TO DISPATCH THEM, AND EACH YEAR FOLLOWING THEIR NUMBERS INCREASE."

AND THE EMPEROR SAID TO SHANG, "WHY DO YOU COMPLAIN? YOU HAVE MUCH WORK FROM MY COURT. IS THIS NOT GOOD FOR SINANJU?"

"NO," REPLIED SHANG. "THIS IS BAD, OR SOON YOU WILL HAVE MORE ENEMIES THAN SUBJECTS. AND IF THE DRAGON THRONE IS TOPPLED, THERE'LL BE NO MORE WORK FOR SINANJU."

"WHAT DO YOU SUGGEST?" INQUIRED THE EMPEROR.

"TAKE THE WOMEN OF YOUR ENEMIES INTO YOUR COURT, MAKE THEM YOURS, THUS BINDING YOUR ENEMIES TO YOU AS SYCOPHANTS."

"YOUR IDEA HAS MERIT, MASTER OF SINANJU. BUT WHAT SHALL I DO WITH MY CONCUBINES? THEY OVERFLOW MY COURT."

"SET THEM FREE," ADVISED SHANG-- WHO LOOKED WITH FAVOR UPON ONE OF THEM. "IT MAY BE I WILL ACCEPT ONE IN PAYMENT FOR MY SERVICE."

AND SO IT WAS DONE. ONE OF THE CONCUBINES, WHO WAS CALLED YEE, RETURNED WITH SHANG TO THE VILLAGE OF SINANJU.

BUT THIS STORY DOES NOT END *HAPPILY*, REMO.

THE MASTER WAS *REVILED* FOR TAKING A CHINESE WOMAN FOR HIS OWN, AND *CORRECTLY SO*--FOR ALL KNOW THAT CHINESE WOMEN ARE NOTORIOUS SHREWS.

RIIIIGHHT...

THIS YEE, HAVING BEEN SPOILED BY PALACE LIFE, FAILED TO APPRECIATE THE MAGNIFICENT SIMPLICITY OF SINANJU. SHE GREW STRIDENT IN HER DEMANDS FOR FOOLISH BAUBLES.

YEE WOULD ASK FOR EMERALDS, AND SHANG WOULD BESTOW THEM.

YEE WOULD ASK FOR RUBIES, AND SHANG WOULD BESTOW THEM. YEE WOULD ASK--

THERE'S A *WORD* FOR SHANG'S PROBLEM.

AND I AM *TELLING* THIS STORY, NOT YOU.

FINALLY, SHANG HAD NO MORE BAUBLES TO GIVE. HE TOLD YEE, "MY WEALTH IS GONE, BUT I AM ENRICHED BY YOUR COMPANIONSHIP."

"IT IS NOT ENOUGH," YEE TOLD HIM. "I DESIRE SOMETHING NO EMPEROR HAS."

SHANG GREW ANGRY. "I HAVE GIVEN YOU ALL I HAVE! WHAT MORE COULD YOU WANT?"

YEE LOOKED BEYOND SHANG'S SHAKING FORM AND A SLY SMILE CAME OVER HER AVARICIOUS FACE.

"ONE THING MORE," YEE SAID, "AND NO MORE."

"BUT IF YOU CANNOT GRANT MY WISH," SHE ADDED, "YOU MUST PROMISE TO RELEASE ME." AND SO SHANG AT LAST UNDERSTOOD THAT YEE DID NOT LOVE HIM.

STILL, HE LOVED HER AND GAVE HIS WORD, ASKING, "WHAT IS YOUR WISH?"

AND YEE POINTED TO THE BRIGHTEST BAUBLE IN THE NIGHT SKY.

"THAT," SHE SAID.

"THE MOON!" SHANG CRIED. "NO ONE CAN GIVE YOU THE MOON! YOU ARE TRYING TO TRICK ME."

"I WILL SETTLE FOR A PIECE OF THE MOON NO BIGGER THAN MY FIST," YEE SAID. "IS THIS TOO MUCH TO ASK?"

FOR DAYS, SHANG DID NOT SLEEP, OR EAT. YEE HAD ASKED THE IMPOSSIBLE, BUT SHANG WAS IN LOVE.

AND SO ONE CLEAR NIGHT, THE MASTER SHANG SET OUT IN SEARCH OF THE MOON.

SHANG WALKED AND WALKED UNTIL THERE WAS NO MORE LAND ON WHICH TO WALK. SO HE FASHIONED A BOAT AND SAILED NORTH.

SHANG AT LENGTH REACHED A SEA CHOKED WITH MOUNTAINS OF ICE, ON WHICH DWELT STRANGE FISH-EATING DOGS, AND BEARS THE COLOR OF SNOW.

FINALLY, SICK WITH HUNGER AND THIRST, MASTER SHANG ENTERED A SEA WHERE THE SUN NEVER SET. HE THOUGHT HIMSELF DEAD, AND DOOMED TO SAIL THE VOID THROUGH ETERNITY.

FINALLY, THE FRAIL CRAFT REACHED A STRANGE LAND.

NOW THIS LAND WAS WHITE, AND THE MOUNTAINS WERE SNOW. EVERYWHERE THERE WAS SNOW, AND UNDER IT ROCK. THE SUN, HANGING LOW IN A TIRED SKY, REFUSED TO SET.

DAYS CAME AND WENT, BUT NO MOON APPEARED. AND MASTER SHANG UNDERSTOOD HE HAD REACHED HIS ULTIMATE GOAL.

HE HAD *WALKED* TO THE MOON, REMO.

HEARTENED, MASTER SHANG ATE THE MEAT OF THE WHITE SWIMMING BEAR AND BROKE OFF A STONE FROM THE MOUNTAINS OF THE MOON.

WITH MEAT TO SUSTAIN HIM, HE SET SAIL FOR THE WORLD AGAIN.

WHEN MONTHS LATER, SHANG HAD RETURNED TO SINANJU, HE TOLD YEE, "I HAVE KEPT MY PROMISE, I HAVE BROUGHT YOU A ROCK OF THE MOON."

AND YEE ACCEPTED THE ROCK AND HIS STORY.

ALTHOUGH SHE CRIED BECAUSE IT MEANT SHE WOULD NEVER SEE HER HOMELAND AGAIN.

BROKEN OF HEART AND IN SPIRIT, HER DAYS WERE NOT LONG AFTER THIS...

AND KNOWING TOO LATE IT WOULD HAVE BEEN BETTER TO LET YEE GO FREE, MASTER SHANG WAS STRICKEN BY GRIEF.

HE TOO DIED, BUT NOT IN SHAME, FOR HE HAD DONE A WONDROUS THING.

TO REMIND FUTURE MASTERS OF THE LESSON OF SHANG, THIS STONE HAS BEEN PASSED DOWN FROM GENERATION TO GENERATION.

IS THAT NOT AN AMAZING STORY, REMO?

CHIUN, I HATE TO BREAK THIS TO YOU, BUT SHANG DIDN'T WALK TO THE MOON.

IT IS *YOU* WHO DO NOT UNDERSTAND, PALE ONE.

SHANG WALKED TO THE *NORTH POLE*. THE WHITE SWIMMING BEARS WERE *POLAR BEARS*. UP THERE, THE SUN DOESN'T *SET* FOR SIX MONTHS.

THAT'S WHY IT NEVER GOT *DARK* AND THERE WAS NO MOON.

YOU *DISAPPOINT* ME, REMO.

GIVE ME *THAT!*

I DO NOT KNOW WHY I BOTHER CASTING *PEARLS* BEFORE A *PALE PIECE OF PIG'S EAR* SUCH AS YOURSELF.

LISTEN... IF SHANG *DID* WALK TO THE MOON, WHY ISN'T HE CONSIDERED A GREAT MASTER? AFTER ALL, NOT *EVERYBODY* JUST WALKS TO THE MOON.

SHANG IS NOT PROPERLY HONORED FOR AN *OBVIOUS* REASON.

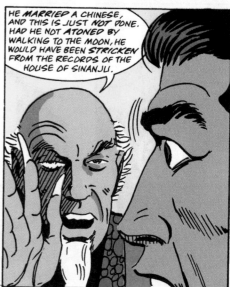

HE *MARRIED* A CHINESE, AND THIS IS JUST *NOT* DONE. HAD HE NOT *ATONED* BY WALKING TO THE MOON, HE WOULD HAVE BEEN *STRICKEN* FROM THE RECORDS OF THE HOUSE OF SINANJU.

161

BRRNG!

IT IS EMPEROR SMITH.

HOW DO YOU KNOW THAT?

IT IS SIMPLE. I AM HERE. YOU ARE HERE. SMITH IS NOT HERE.

THERE-FORE, IT IS SMITH.

WHAT ELSE DO YOU FORESEE, KARNAK?

BRING!

I CAN FORESEE...

... WHICH OF US WILL ANSWER THE PHONE.

YEAH? WHO?

YOU, REMO.

BRRING!

WHAT MAKES YOU SAY THAT?

IT IS SIMPLE. BECAUSE I AM NOT GOING TO. ≶ HEH HEH ≶ I AM NOT GOING TO.

OH, YOU'RE HILARIOUS. YOU OUGHTA BE ON CARSON.

AND YOU ARE STILL GULLIBLE. AMAZING... IT IS A WONDER REMO SURVIVED THIS LONG...

BRRING!

GET YOUR PENCIL AND PAPER READY, GUYS AND GALS, 'CAUSE WE'VE GOT A TREAT FOR YOU. IN THE SAME MIGHTY MARVEL MANNER THAT BROUGHT YOU *HOW TO DRAW COMICS THE MARVEL WAY,* WE NOW--

ENOUGH OF YOUR PRATTLE, WHITE PENCILIST. GET ON WITH YOUR TEST.

TEST?

YES, TEST. NOW BEGIN, PRETENDER!

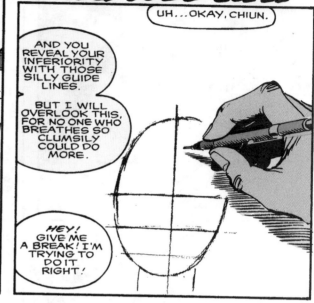

UH...OKAY, CHIUN.

AND YOU REVEAL YOUR INFERIORITY WITH THOSE SILLY GUIDE LINES.

BUT I WILL OVERLOOK THIS, FOR NO ONE WHO BREATHES SO CLUMSILY COULD DO MORE.

HEY! GIVE ME A BREAK! I'M TRYING TO DO IT RIGHT!

I UNDERSTAND. YOU ARE AN ARTIST. I WILL WATCH QUIETLY UNTIL YOU ARE FINISHED.

PAH! ONLY ONE WITH ROUND EYES WOULD SEE MY MAGNIFICENT HAIR AS A BRUSH TO CLEAN FLOORS WITH.

I WILL CLOSE MY EYES AND WHEN I OPEN THEM AGAIN, YOU WILL HAVE ELIMINATED THIS MOCKERY.

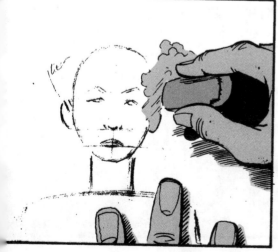

NOW YOU INSULT ME WITH THE WRINKLES OF A HAIRLESS DOG!

FORGIVE ME, CHI-- MASTER CHIUN. I'M KINDA NERVOUS.

A PITIFUL EXCUSE, BUT THE MASTER OF SINANJU IS ALWAYS REASONABLE.

WITH ALL THE WONDERFUL KOREAN ARTISTS AVAILABLE, I STILL FIND IT INEXPLICABLE THAT YOUR EDITOR INSISTS ON HIRING LOWLY AMERICANS.

I WILL TAKE THIS MATTER UP--

AEEIN!

ONE WHO HAS MASTERED THE SUN SOURCE WOULD NOT BE CAUGHT DEAD IN SUCH RAGS.

INSTEAD OF ONE GRACEFUL GARMENT, YOU GIVE ME TWO NOT FIT TO CARRY WASTE IN! SUCH LACK OF RESPECT CANNOT BE TOLERATED!

AW, LIGHTEN UP. I'M UNDER A DEADLI--

GAKK!

DRAW NO MORE, WHELP.

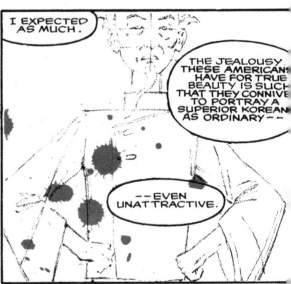

I EXPECTED AS MUCH.

THE JEALOUSY THESE AMERICANS HAVE FOR TRUE BEAUTY IS SUCH THAT THEY CONNIVE TO PORTRAY A SUPERIOR KOREAN AS ORDINARY--

--EVEN UNATTRACTIVE.

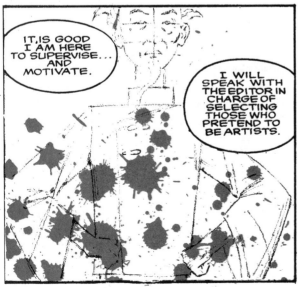

IT IS GOOD I AM HERE TO SUPERVISE... AND MOTIVATE.

I WILL SPEAK WITH THE EDITOR IN CHARGE OF SELECTING THOSE WHO PRETEND TO BE ARTISTS.

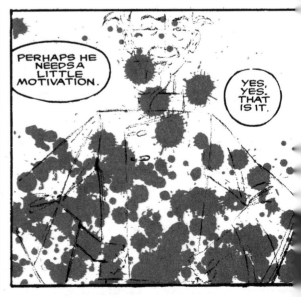

PERHAPS HE NEEDS A LITTLE MOTIVATION.

YES, YES. THAT IS IT.